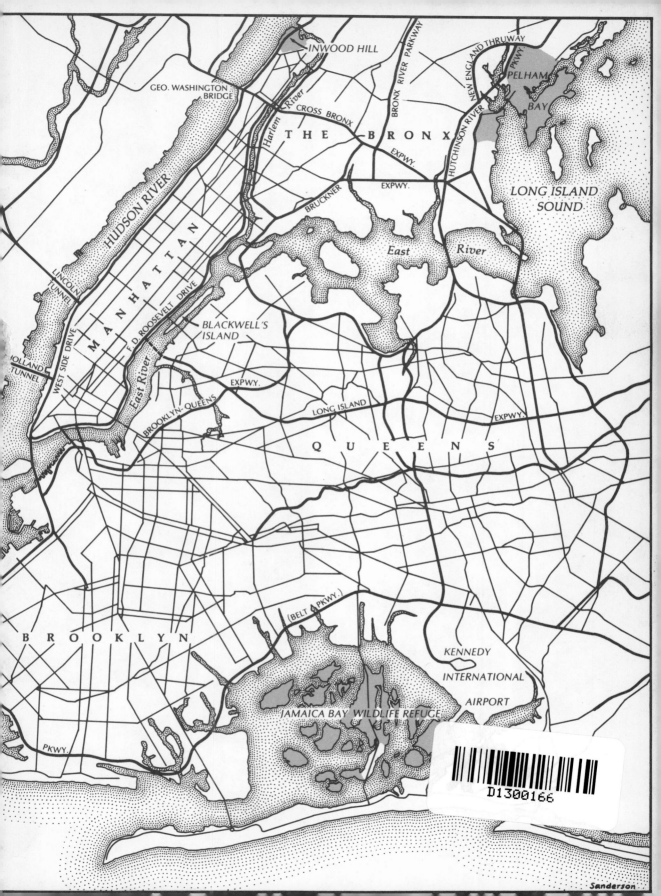

INWOOD HILL

GEO. WASHINGTON BRIDGE

Harlem River

CROSS BRONX

BRONX RIVER PARKWAY

NEW ENGLAND THRUWAY

Hutchinson River

PELHAM
BAY
PKWY.

THE BRONX

EXPWY.

EXPWY.

Bruckner

LONG ISLAND
SOUND

East   River

HUDSON RIVER

LINCOLN
TUNNEL

M A N H A T T A N

F. D. ROOSEVELT DRIVE

BLACKWELL'S
ISLAND

WEST SIDE DRIVE

HOLLAND
TUNNEL

East River

BROOKLYN- QUEENS

EXPWY.

LONG ISLAND

EXPWY.

Q U E E N S

B R O O K L Y N

(BELT PKWY.)

KENNEDY
INTERNATIONAL
AIRPORT

JAMAICA BAY WILDLIFE REFUGE

PKWY.

Sanderson

The Forests and Wetlands
of New York City

The Forests and Wetlands of New York City

by Elizabeth Barlow

Little, Brown and Company · Boston · Toronto

Sections of this book previously appeared in *New York Magazine, Smithsonian* and *Audubon Magazine.*

Published simultaneously in Canada by Little, Brown & Company (Canada) Limited
PRINTED IN THE UNITED STATES OF AMERICA

For Ed

CONTENTS

MAPS

Richard Sanderson, cartographer

ILLUSTRATIONS

FOREWORD

The word "environment" now evokes night-mares. It calls to mind the various forms of pollution, crowding and noise, the depletion of natural resources, the thousand devils of the ecologic crisis. There are indeed good reasons for being preoccupied with the damage done by technology and the population avalanche; environmental degradation inevitably results in a debased quality of human existence. But our lives will become increasingly dismal if we put exclusive emphasis on these negative aspects of the environmental problem. The management of nature should be concerned with not only the ecologic crisis but also the preservation and creation of positive values.

The widespread interest in the conservation of primeval scenery indicates that nature and especially wilderness constitute values which must be considered along with comfort and other utilitarian aspects of life. In practice, however, many people have little or no opportunity to experience and enjoy nature except near their own locality of residence. For this reason, it is not sufficient to save the redwoods, the Everglades, and as many other areas of distant wilderness as possible; it is equally important to protect nature in urban areas; figuratively speaking, we must improve Coney Island.

We must, of course, eliminate pollutants, dirt, and noise from parks, waterfronts, and waterways. We must be given once more the opportunity to experience the Milky Way on cloudless nights and fragrance of flowers in spring. But Elizabeth Barlow goes far beyond that in *The Forests and Wetlands of New York City,* where she describes in picturesque and illuminating details the natural riches that are still available to New York City residents. From historical and scientific documents, she extracts the positive values that are inherent in the natural milieu of New York City, and the manner in which these potential values can be converted into existential reality.

Ancient peoples personified localities with particular gods or goddesses. We no longer believe in dryads or nymphs, but rationalists as we may be, we still respond to phrases such as "the genius of New England" or "the spirit of the Far West." Our very use of these phrases implies the acknowledgment that each place or region is characterized by a set of attributes that makes it different from others and accounts for its individuality. Elizabeth Barlow's book deals precisely with the spirit or genius of the New York City area, defined not by the characters of its inhabitants, art, and commerce, but by its natural history. As she points out, the geologic skeleton of New York is so diversified and well articulated that this alone would suffice to endow the city with physiognomic uniqueness. But the urban area acquires still further interest for the lover of scenery and nature from the fact that it constitutes the border between two plant zones — southern trees mixing in many places with the maples, beeches, birches, and hemlocks of New England. Much of this diversified natural history persists in the city's parks and wetlands. Inwood Hill provides striking evidence of the resilience of nature since it is still beautifully forested despite occupation and exploitation of the area by many different kinds of people during many local and destructive wars.

Even more interesting is the fact that some of the city's natural environments, which appeared at a time to have been spoiled beyond repair, have been restored to a state of biological richness and beauty by conscious human effort. The bird refuge in Jamaica Bay, for example, is not the original landscape, but one re-created by the lifework of a devoted Parks Department employee. The return to Jamaica Bay of the glossy ibis and the snowy egret is a beautiful symbol of the natural richness that can be brought back to urban areas by intelligent and persistent human effort. In fact, one of the most appealing aspects of Elizabeth Barlow's book is her description of the highly personal attitudes of individual persons in all walks of life toward particular spots of the New York City parks and wetlands.

The Forests and Wetlands of New York City is thus much more than an enjoyable and illuminating guide to the history and present state of nature in our city. It demonstrates that, while man is all too often a destroyer of wilderness, he can also shape and restore the natural world — and perhaps even improve on it by giving existential expression to the genius of the place.

René Dubos

The Rockefeller University
New York City

INTRODUCTION

The critics and celebrants of New York are legion. New York is probably the most critically self-conscious, scrupulously analyzed, praised and damned city in the world. For the most part it is the wonderful and fearful conglomeration of human activity and human artifacts — people and things — that gets written about. There is, of course, another New York underlying this hive of economic, artistic and civic enterprise, the New York of rivers and sea, of firm bedrock and salt marsh–fringed shores. And were it not for this other New York — geophysical New York — socioeconomic New York would never have come into being.

The great port exists because of the protective, womblike configuration of the city's harbor; its easily defended, constricted Narrows entrance was sculpted by glacial deposits. The skyscraper was born in New York because its footings could be safely anchored in the city's extremely tough bedrock, a bedrock composed of the stumps of an ancient mountain chain that had been eroded away over the millennia. These were the generative forces, the natural agents that gave the city its unique form which is at the same time both fantastic and logical.

The city's growth, and indeed its health, depended in the past as they do now on natural forces, a fact that we in our technocentric pride sometimes forget. Like ancient Rome, New York is umbilically linked by an aqueduct system to a mountainous watershed area in the north. As this system, which in a less populous time appeared to supply water in limitless abundance, approaches capacity, new methods of securing potable water from the rivers or the sea will have to be found. Now it takes only a relatively minor drought to bring home the city's immense dependence on this most basic of all natural resources.

Too often nature and the city are thought of as separate and opposite, and we fail to see the relentless dynamic of the natural process operating all around, within the city as well as without. Rain and snow fall indiscriminately, performing their ancient function as agents of erosion; in the city the surfaces they abrade are building stone and pavement instead of soil and bedrock. Wherever it can, nature insinuates itself into the urban fabric. Wildflowers spring up through cracks in concrete, and vacant lots are never vacant for long as weeds and grasses and even trees put down roots in the thin, rubbly soil.

Transformed, depressed, subdued, nature has by no means been eradicated in New York. It is, of course, most observable in those preserved pockets of open space — the city's parks, where the remnants of the native ecology, though modified by more than three centuries of human occupation or proximity, still exist. It may be said that the parks are the Rosetta stones of the city's ecological patrimony.

That there are still wild and wooded spots in the metropolis and fragments of natural, unspoiled shoreline seems surprising to those whose image of New York is focused on Manhattan, that glittering assemblage of steel and glass and concrete, river-cordoned so that it stands discrete, emphatic, like some giant improbable ship, all hard-edged and clearly delineated, aggressively artificial in a way that other cities with a broader land base are not. But New York is more than Manhattan, and even Manhattan has something approaching wilderness in Inwood Hill Park, perched on its steep, northernmost promonotory where pheasants nest and an occasional red fox prowls on the slopes once occupied by Indians and later by Hessian mercenaries.

Manhattan has Central Park, too, probably the most beloved and jealously guarded piece of urban open space in the world, an everyman's backyard. But Central Park does not feature in this book because its story has already been well told (by Henry Hope Reed and Sophia Duckworth in *Central Park: A History and a Guide,* New York, 1967) and that story has more to do with the history of landscape architecture and the genius of Frederick Law Olmsted than with the native ecology of New York City. (This is not to say that Olmsted did not respect the city's natural endowment when he laid out Central Park, an early example of the "naturalistic park": informal, rustic-seeming, heavily reliant on native plant species.) For the same reasons Olmsted's other great landscape creation, Prospect Park in Brooklyn is not included here; it deserves, and has got, a separate volume of its own (Clay Lancaster, *Prospect Park Handbook,* New York, 1967).

There are several sizable forests and wetlands in the boroughs outside Manhattan: from the air they appear as green islands in an urban sea. The Bronx is park-rich, if such a term can be appropriately applied to so populous an area, a circumstance attributable to the foresighted purchase of a series of large-scale "parks beyond the Harlem" together with an interconnecting system of parkways in the days before the Bronx was part of New York City. Van Cortlandt Park, Bronx Park — famous as the home of the New York Zoological Society and the New York Botanical Garden — and Pelham Bay Park, facing Long Island Sound, were the principal parcels of the purchase. Pelham Bay has been singled out for treatment here, although for springtime rambles the Bronx Park with its rushing river and beautiful virgin stand of hemlock forest has an incomparable beauty. Van Cortlandt, also neglected in these pages, is the starting point of the old Croton Aqueduct Trail and site of a lovely bird- and flora-teeming swamp, which was for many years a favorite haunt of John Kieran, chronicler of the natural history of New York City. "Poor old Van," moans Richard Edes Harrison, another longtime New York City park lover, who recalls Van Cortlandt when it was still intact before being carved up by the Major Deegan Expressway.

Alley Park in Queens, another motor-dissected park, was once Alley

Pond Park, but the word "pond" dropped out of the title of the park because the pond with its colonial grist mill, post office and general store dropped out of existence when the interchange for the Long Island and Cross Island expressways was built. The quadrant of the park facing Little Neck Bay is now much despoiled, a marsh-*cum*-garbage dump. It holds an interesting attraction for ecologists, however: in winter owls roost in the tall trees of the upland beside the bay in convenient proximity to the mice and rats that are attracted to the garbage. The upland part of Alley Park marks the southern edge of glacial advance into the New York City area; here the rolling morainal terrain is covered with deep forest punctuated by small glacial ponds, their shimmering stillness rippled here and there by the balletic touch of a dragonfly. In spite of its richness as a resource for naturalists (and anyone else who relishes the sensuous mystery of quiet, dim, tree-canopied places), Alley Park has been omitted from this book because its ecology is more or less a repetition of that of the Staten Island greenbelt, that hilly central spine, which is also a legacy of the glacier's terminus.

Staten Island is looked at here not just for the sake of its beautiful wooded greenbelt, but in its entirety as a phenomenon of sudden, almost violent transition from a quiet slumbering collection of semirural communities into something that will someday soon be a densely developed, almost continuous urban mass. The catalyst for its development was the construction of the Verrazano-Narrows Bridge, which gave the island swift and easy access to the rest of New York (and vice versa) and simultaneously made it a major corridor of movement from New Jersey to Long Island.

Where New York presents a flank to the beating surf of the Atlantic, the white sands of the Rockaway Peninsula stretch out forming a barrier beach. Sheltered behind these protective sands are the calm, grassy waters of Jamaica Bay. Jamaica Bay — so airy and expansive, so pleasantly empty of everything except birds and airplanes overhead and old men and boys fishing off the sides of bridges and trawlers and pleasure boats docked along the wharves of numerous marinas, an incongruous but happy amalgam of many things; salty honky-tonk, serious ornithology, lazy angling and jet travel.

Jamaica Bay's glory is its wildlife refuge, a reconstructed natural area

Alley Pond, 1932.

Site of Alley Pond, today.

where a profuse marine vegetation has been coaxed back into existence on desolated sandbars. Its story is offered here as a parable to give optimism and hope to those who feel that the relationship between man and his environment is headed on a one-way course downhill.

Another kind of parable is the story of Welfare Island. According to plans, the island is to be a combination model community and environmental education center. As presently envisioned, the proposed ecological park will be programmed to demonstrate the ways in which man affects and is affected by basic environmental forces: air, sunlight, water, gravity.

It is with the pre-urban New York City habitats that this book begins: the vision of the city before it was a city, when it was only a wilderness, awesomely magnificent, blessedly endowed with an abundance of game and edible vegetation, as incomparable a natural resource as the modern city is an artifact. Following this portrait of the virgin landscape is a two-chapter examination of causality: the geological forces that brought topographical New York into being and the corresponding modification of climate and plant communities that produced the landscape of forests and wetlands that form the backdrop for man's brief three-hundred-year history on the New York scene. Finally, there are the remnants, the forests and wetlands of today and their constituencies, the people who use and love them. It is to these constituencies that I acknowledge a large debt of gratitude; not only did they generously provide me with information, but with many pleasant, companionable days spent out of doors.

From Eric Haas, a longtime Inwood resident, I learned a great deal about trees while enjoying a late fall picnic of apples and banana bread as we sat on top of Inwood Hill. Another woodsman, a Parks Department horticulturist and Boy Scout troup leader, Joseph Melston, conducted me on a tour of the Inwood forest on a brilliant, bitingly cold day when thick, fresh snow lay on the ground.

Dr. Theodore Kazimiroff, the encyclopedically informed Bronx historian and naturalist, gave me a helpful tour of the salt marsh at Pelham Bay. Visiting Pelham Bay Park several times alone in midsummer, I spoke with many people — the "regulars," whose intimacy with the park gave me insights both historical and sociological — and I thank them collectively.

I spent a delightful and strangely poignant summer day roaming Staten Island with the naturalist and pioneer wildlife photographer Howard Cleaves, whose residency on the island dates from 1901 and who is a witness to its inexorable transformation from bucolic oasis to modern suburb. I was privileged also to follow the dynamic Mathilde Weingartner leading a tour of schoolchildren through the William T. Davis Wildlife Refuge on an early fall day when the first leaves were turning. My thanks go also to the staff of High Rock Conservation Center, who were very cordial and helpful on several visits there, and to Loring McMillan, director of the Staten Island Historical Society, for sharing with me his wide-ranging knowledge of the island's history and ecology.

For many enlightening trips to Jamaica Bay at all seasons of the year I especially thank Herbert Johnson, Parks Department superintendent, who deserves sole credit for the construction of the beautiful wildlife refuge, his life's handiwork.

In addition, I owe thanks to Mrs. May Milstein, public relations director at Bird S. Coler Hospital, for making available to me her ample file of newspaper clippings on Welfare Island. Although Alley Park does not receive a separate chapter here, I am grateful to Samuel Yeaton of the Queens County Bird Club for sharing with me his extensive knowledge of that park and also to Mrs. Joan Rosner of the New York City Board of Education, who supervises an excellent program of nature education there.

Besides the people who have shared their knowledge of individual parks, I wish to thank the "generalists": those natural scientists, members of the conservation fraternity and park professionals who have given me assistance and encouragement. Dr. Christopher J. Schuberth of the American Museum of Natural History has been an invaluable resource on the city's geology, and Dr. Leslie A. Sirkin of Adelphi University supplied me with useful information on the city's paleobotany. I have drawn on Richard Edes Harrison, cartographer and naturalist, for his longtime intimate knowledge of the city's parks. For an informed naturalist's eye on a number of field trips I thank Mary Thacher.

I give special thanks to Parks Department employees Arthur Murphy, landscape architect in charge of tree planting, Cornelius M. O'Shea, Manhattan borough horticulturist, and Raymond J. Glespen, of public relations.

I am grateful also to the librarians of the New-York Historical Society for their courteous and informative assistance.

My final and greatest debt of gratitude, extending back over the past six years that I have lived in New York City, is to the Parks Council for the resources of its office and the friendship and inspiration of its staff and fellow members, particularly its recent presidents Whitney North Seymour, Jr., James Sheldon Oliensis, Adele Auchincloss, and Edward Hallam Tuck.

The Forests and Wetlands of New York City

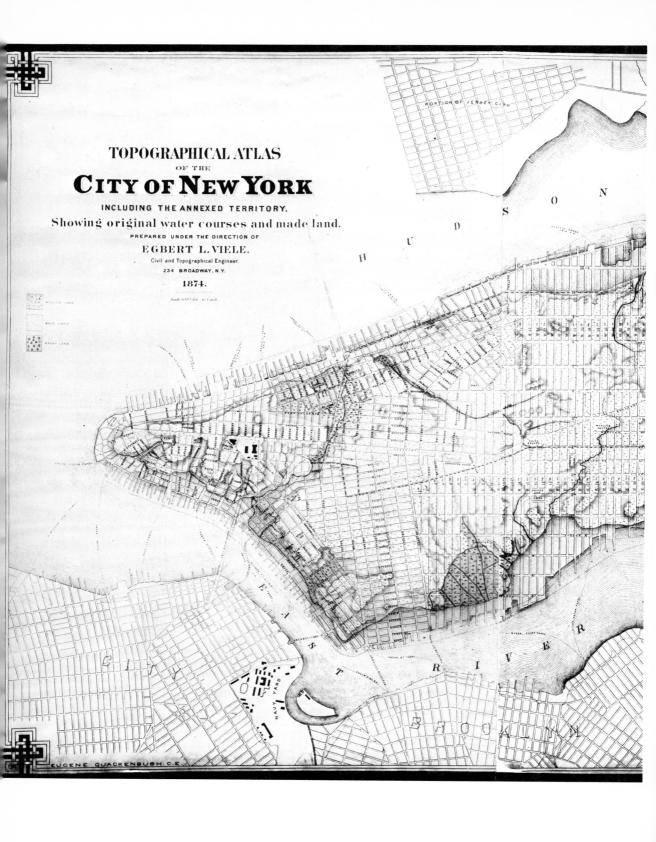

TOPOGRAPHICAL ATLAS
OF THE
CITY OF NEW YORK
INCLUDING THE ANNEXED TERRITORY,
Showing original water courses and made land.
PREPARED UNDER THE DIRECTION OF
EGBERT L. VIELE.
Civil and Topographical Engineer.
234 BROADWAY, N.Y.
1874.

Scale 1000 feet to 1 inch

EUGENE QUACKENBUSH, C.E.

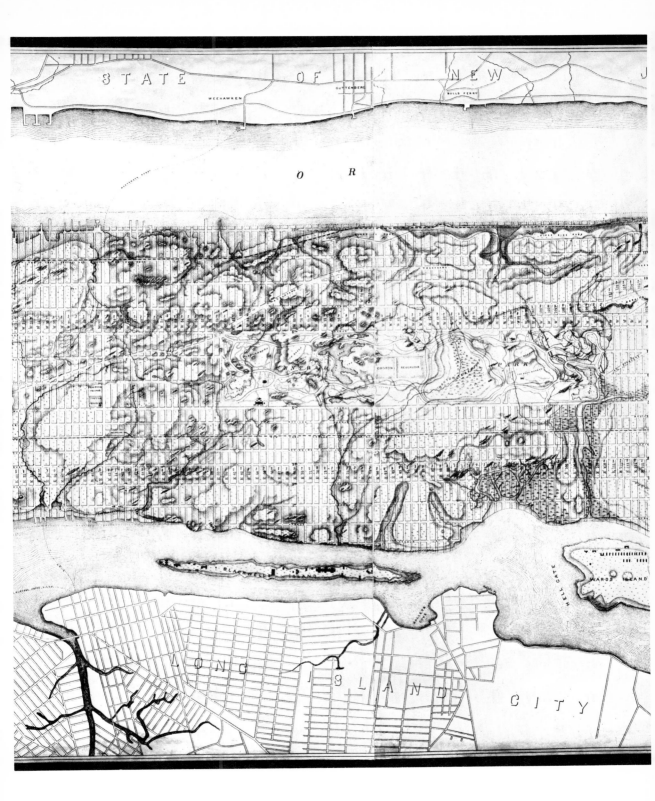

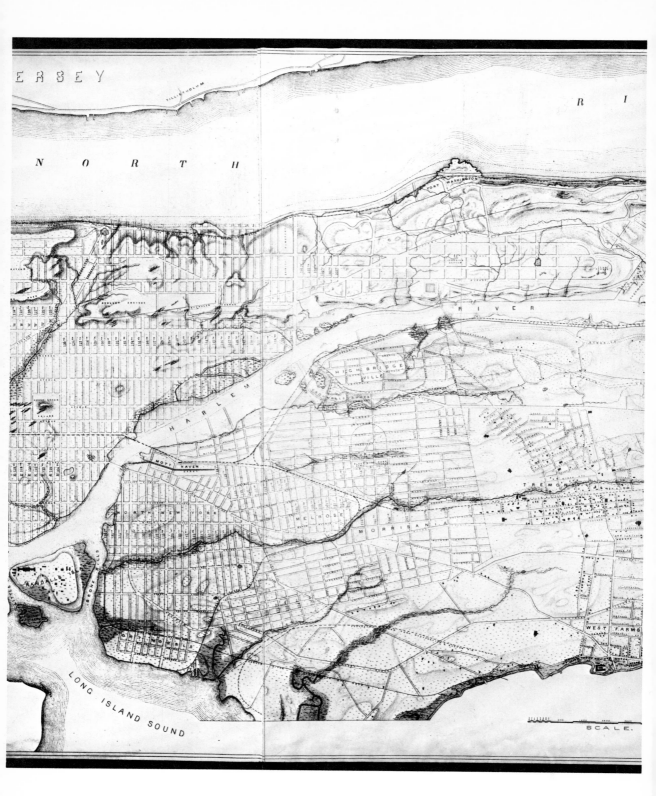

CITY OF YONKERS

WEST VINCENT

RIVERDALE

INWOOD

SPUYTEN DUYVIL

BRIDGE

PARADE GROUND

WOODLAWN CEMETERY

FORDHAM

WILLIAMS BRIDGE

WESTCHESTER COUNTY

LONG ISLAND SOUND

BRONX RIVER

WOODLAWN

SECTION ACROSS CENTRAL PARK

SECTION FROM 59TH STREET TO BROOKLYN HEIGHTS

SECTION FROM HOBOKEN TO BROOKLYN

1

THE GREEN BREAST

As the moon rose higher the inessential houses began to melt away until gradually I became aware of the old island here that flowered once for Dutch sailors' eyes — a fresh, green breast of the new world. Its vanished trees . . . had once pandered in whispers to the last and greatest of all human dreams; for a transitory enchanted moment man must have held his breath in the presence of this continent, compelled into an aesthetic contemplation he neither understood nor desired, face to face for the last time in history with something commensurate to his capacity for wonder.

— *F. Scott Fitzgerald*
The Great Gatsby

Every morning people pour out of my apartment building and file to the bus stop on the corner of East End Avenue and Seventy-ninth Street. Only a few decades ago, Seventy-ninth Street was a dusty road, and where the crosstown bus sits idling a little spring poured out of the ground. Just below Sloan's Supermarket, where I buy groceries, another spring gushed forth. Both springs belonged to Marston's Creek, one of the many brooks and rivulets that once coursed across the East Side of Manhattan. In fact, everywhere up and down the length of the island where today streams of people rush to meet subways and busses there were once streams of water rushing to meet the sea. There was Cedar Creek emptying into the East River at what is now Seventeenth Street; the Saw Kill flowing through the swamp that later became the Reservoir in Central Park; Montayne's Rivulet running through Harlem to its mouth at Hell Gate Bay; Sherman Creek draining the waters of the high Fort Washington ridge into the Harlem River. There were Minetta

Old Arch Brook on the old Riker estate, East River and
Seventy-fifth Street. Drawing by Eliza Greatorex, 1869.

Brook flowing through Greenwich Village and many tiny rills that spilled over the rocky ledges of the Upper West Side, cascading into the Hudson.

Now, invisibly, these water courses flow on as underground sewers; their old beds have been geometricized in conformity with the grid of streets above them. In the Bronx, Tibbetts Brook, which feeds the Van Cortlandt swamp, becomes, after draining the swamp, the Spuyten Duyvil outlet sewer. John Kieran remembers when "Tibbetts Brook ran aboveground through cattail marshes and wet meadows all the way from the lake outlet to the old northern loop of the Harlem River, crossing Broadway at about 240th Street en route and providing several good swimming holes to which I gave my patronage as a schoolboy."

Even when they have not been undergrounded, the old brooks are still sewers, or rather sewer outfalls. In southern Brooklyn and Queens the tidal creeks where fresh waters used to mingle with the incoming tides are now conduits discharging the effluent from six municipal sewerage treatment plants into Jamaica Bay. Though contours have been straightened

4

and bottoms dredged, the ancient, historically evocative names, often Dutch-donated, linger on: Paerdegat Basin, Barbadoes Basin, Conch Basin, Mill Basin, Shellbank Creek and Mott Hook.

Two early Dutch travelers, Jasper Danckaerts and Peter Sluyter, enjoyed oysters, some measuring a foot long, from what is today the anaerobic Gowanus Canal. Newtown Creek, Brooklyn's other industrial sewer, still retains at its head a now anachronistically named little promontory, Mussel Island.

Besides carving channels across the face of New York the old streams scalloped its shores, giving the waterfront a much more sinuous perimeter than it has today. Then, instead of the taut perimeter ruled by the Army Corps of Engineers' pierhead and bulkhead lines, the shores were everywhere indented with little bays and tidal estuaries. Instead of a firm seawall there were large salt meadow marshes which were daily bathed as the incoming tides washed over their fine mat of cordgrasses.

Prominently penetrating colonial Manhattan was the Graught, a marsh inlet later covered by Broad Street. The beavers that once built their dams along its banks are memorialized today in a financial district address: Beaver Street. Memorialized too are the girls who once spread out their laundry to dry on the grassy banks beside the pebble-bottomed little brook that later became Maagde Paetje, or Maiden Lane.

Manhattan was not only more irregular in outline but also a good deal narrower in those days. Like growth rings on a tree, earth fill has over the years been deposited in encircling bands around the southern end of the island until now Water Street is five hundred feet from the East River and Greenwich Street, once the waterfront thoroughfare on the west, is the same distance from the Hudson. Where Kennedy Airport juts a concrete apron into Jamaica Bay there were once only water and a vast tide-inundated marsh. Soundview Park in the East Bronx, Marine Park in Brooklyn and Great Kills Park on Staten Island are also "reclaimed" marshlands — that is to say, phased-out garbage dumps.

The early Dutch settlers gravitated to the flat marsh-fringed lowlands reminiscent of the topography of Holland. In addition to New Amsterdam in lower Manhattan they formed villages bordering on other New York City wetlands: Flatbush and Flatlands in Brooklyn where the Canarsie salt meadows stretched out to embrace Jamaica Bay; Nieu Haarlem on

5

the *muscoota,* or marshy plain, that covered eastern Manhattan north of
110th Street; and Nieu Dorp beside the Great Kills marshes on Staten
Island.

The Indians were marsh men, too, weaving trails through the cordgrasses as they went back and forth to their fishing stations. Archaeologists have found evidence of their occupation in the shell heaps beside the
Bartow Creek tidal inlet (obliterated by dredging for the Olympic rowing
basin in the 1950's) in Pelham Bay Park; in the ovens or steaming holes
filled with shells and other fragments (covered over by ball fields in the
1930's) near Spuyten Duyvil at Inwood Park; and in the burial chambers
and extensive collections of artifacts (now a garbage dump) bordering the
south shore of Staten Island and the Fresh Kills marshes.

The Indians' main trail, which led from strongholds in the Bronx and
their camp at Inwood Hill down to the little colonial village with its
wooden houses huddled up against the sides of the fort, did not skirt the
shore, but ran through the Manhattan forest along the line of present-day
Broadway. In the days before the Dutch had staked out their claim to
lower Manhattan the Indians had camped on the western bank of Collect
Pond, a large, clear spring-fed water body some forty feet deep where the
Criminal Court building now stands. They left a large deposit of shells,
and the mound they had occupied the Dutch named Kalchhook (Shell-
point). The name "Collect" is thought to be perhaps a corruption of
"Kalchhook," or perhaps simply a denotation of the collection of springs
that irrigated the pond. The English called it Freshwater Pond and drew
their water from one of its primary sources, the Tea-water Spring, so
named because of its reputation for being the best drinking water on the
island. Carts would form long traffic-obstructing queues at the Tea-water
pump, which stood where Park Row and Pearl Street now intersect.

The pond was drained by two marsh-bordered streams: the eastern,
called Old Wreck Brook, ran through Wolfert's Marsh into a bay now
covered by the approach ramps of the Brooklyn Bridge; the western,
flowing through the Lispenard Meadows, followed the line of, and later
became, the canal that gave Canal Street its name. When the tide was
high the waters of the East River and the Hudson commingled in this
marsh system, and Manhattan became in effect two islands instead of one.

In colonial times Collect Pond was famous for its fishing. It was so

6

Hudson River at Manhattanville, an oil painting by Victor Gifford Audubon, son of John James Audubon, circa 1845.

Collect Pond, 1800.

popular, in fact, that in 1734 the town fathers passed an ordinance forbidding net fishing or the catching of fish "by any other engine, machine, arts, ways or means whatsoever, other than by angling with angle rod, hook and line only." The fine for ignoring this law was twenty shillings. Later the pond played a role in the history of navigation: in 1796, seven years before Fulton's *Clermont,* the world's first steamship was given a trial run on its waters.

By this time, however, water pollution had come to New York, and Collect Pond was badly polluted, a health hazard. Its refuse-laden waters stank with the bodies of dead animals. The old Kalchhook on the pond's western edge had acquired an infamous reputation, first as the spot where in 1741 a Negro rebellion had been quelled and the participants hanged and burned, and later as the site of the public gallows. In 1808 it was leveled and its rubble was used to fill in the pond. Streets were laid out, with present-day Centre Street running down the middle of the former pond. The miry Lispenard Meadows, where straying cattle had sometimes become trapped in the soft marsh ooze, were drained, and the tree-bordered canal was constructed.

The area where Collect Pond had stood soon gained a notoriety even greater than that it had had during its latter days as a pond. It became a place of filthy, crowded tenements sheltering the most degraded, gin-soaked element of Victorian society. Charles Dickens, visiting America in 1842, made a point of touring the area in the company of two policemen. He wrote: "Debauchery has made the very houses prematurely old. See how rotten beams are tumbling down, and how the patched and broken windows seem to scowl dimly, like eyes that have been hurt in drunken frays."

Not only had New York begun to have serious slum-bred social ills; the physical health of all its people was being jeopardized to an ever increasing degree by water pollution. Contamination of the Collect had foreshadowed the general contamination of the city's water sources. Yellow fever epidemics took a calamitous toll. Today's Washington Square and Madison Square were originally set aside as Potter's fields to receive the bodies of plague victims. Still, the population continued to grow and was fast outstripping the remaining clean springs and wells. The year that Dickens visited America turned out to be a jubilee year for New York, for on

October 14 the Croton Aqueduct was opened, carrying pure water into the Central Park Reservoir from the mountains of northern Westchester and Putnam counties. For days people celebrated the miracle, turning on the new spigots with continual fascination, toasting themselves and their town with the clear, tasteless, odorless water that came out. From the mid-nineteenth century on, New York was no longer a self-contained economic unit, and its concentrated population owed its sustenance to an ever expanding hinterland, depending to a growing degree not only on distant watersheds but on increasingly distant food sources as well.

The urban ills of Dickens's day, though pernicious, were highly localized, and for the most part New York was still a pleasant and very beautiful place to live. Dickens wrote that "the country around New York is surpassingly and exquisitely picturesque." He added that "The climate is somewhat of the warmest. What would it be, without the sea breezes which come from its beautiful bay in the eveningtime, I will not throw myself or my readers into a fever by inquiring."

Earlier journalists had also remarked on the New York climate. Reverend Charles Wolley, writing of his stay in the city from 1668 to 1670, declared, "It's a Climate of a Sweet and wholesome breath, free from those annoyances which are commonly ascribed by Naturalists for the insalubriety of any Country, *viz.* South or South-east winds, many stagnant Waters, lowness of shoars, inconstancy of Weather, and the excessive heat of the Summer; the extremity of which is gently refresh'd, fann'd and allay'd by constant breezes from the Sea."

Adrian Van der Donck, an early patroon, said: "The air in the New-Netherlands is so dry, sweet and healthy that we need not wish that it were otherwise . . . There are no heavy damps or stinking mists in the country, and if any did arise, a northerly breeze would blow them away, and purify the air. The summer heat is not oppressive in the warmest weather, for it is mitigated by the sea breezes, the northerly winds, and by showers."

Just as the sea breezes refreshed the land, so the breezes blowing off the land carried land odors to the ships at sea. Daniel Denton, an early resident of Jamaica, Queens, wrote that "The Countrey itself sends forth such a fragrant smell that it may be perceived at sea before [the ships] make the land."

The fragrance of the air was noticed by Jasper Danckaerts and his traveling companion Peter Sluyter in their wanderings around New Netherlands in 1678. "In passing through this island," wrote Danckaerts of Manhattan, "we sometimes encountered such a sweet smell in the air that we stood still, because we did not know what it was we were meeting."

Perfuming the air were a profuse native vegetation and many fruit trees which the Dutch had planted in their boweries. "As we walked along," said Danckaerts, "we saw in different gardens trees full of apples of various kinds, and so laden with peaches and other fruit that one might doubt whether there were more leaves or fruit on them." Van der Donck said that peaches were so plentiful that branches frequently broke under their weight. He went on to list other fruits which the skilled Dutch arboriculturists had brought with them to New Netherlands: "Morecotoons [a kind of peach], apricots, several sorts of the best plums, almonds, persimmons, cornelian cherries, figs, several sorts of currants, gooseberries, calissiens, and thorn apples."

Nature's own garden was equally bountiful. According to Daniel Denton, "The Fruits natural to [Long] Island are Mulberries, Posimons, Grapes great and small, Huckelberries, Cramberries, Plums of several sorts, Rosberries and Strawberries, of which last is such abundance in June, that the Fields and Woods are died red: Which the Countrey-people perceiving, instantly arm themselves with bottles of Wine, Cream, and Sugar and instead of a Coat of Male, every one takes a Female upon his Horse behind him, and so rushing violently into the fields, never leave till they have disrob'd them of their red colours, and turned them into the old habit."

Besides the fruits of the field there were flowers which Denton extolled with equal ardor: "Yea in May you shall see the Woods and Fields so curiously bedecke with Roses, and with an innumerable multitude of delightful Flowers . . . that you may behold Nature contending with Art, and striving to equal, if not excell many Gardens in England."

In colonial times tall forests covered much of the land that was to become New York City. The native trees observed by Robert Juet, who was an officer on the *Half Moon* in 1609 when Henry Hudson made his famous voyage up the river that was later named for him, were a "great store of

Rock outcroppings of northern Manhattan, as seen in a water color by George Holston, 1875.

goodly Oakes, and Wal-nut trees, and Chest-nut trees, ewe trees, and trees of sweet wood in great abundance." On Daniel Denton's Long Island there were "oaks white and red, Walnut trees, Chestnut trees . . . Maples, Cedars, Saxifrage, Beach, Birch, Holly, Hazel, with many sorts more."

So extensive and prolific were the forests when the first settlers arrived that Van der Donck complained: "The whole country is covered with Wood, and in our manner of speaking, there is all too much of it, and in our way. Still it comes to hand to build vessels and houses, and to enclose the farms, &c. . . . The land also is so natural to produce wood, that in a few years large trees will be grown, which I can say with certainty from my own observation, and that unless there be natural changes of great improvidence, there can be no scarcity of wood in this country."

Every New Yorker is familiar with the rock outcroppings in Central Park. Once New York was studded as far south as Thirtieth Street with surface protrusions of the tough, durable stone known as Manhattan schist. As New York's skyscrapers today impress visitors from abroad, so the rocks themselves awed early voyagers like Danckaerts, who speaks of "ridges of high rocks, displaying themselves very majestically and inviting all men to acknowledge in them the majesty, grandeur, power and glory of their Creator."

Between two rock outcroppings at the north end of Central Park was McGown's Pass, where the old trunk trail of the Indians, renamed the King's Way (later the Albany Post Road or Great Post Road), ran into the wilds of northern Manhattan. Rising out of the swampy Harlem *muscoota* was Slag Berg (or Snake Hill), known today as Mount Morris, with the little village of New Harlem nestled at its base. To the west, overlooking the Hudson, was a long, narrow escarpment, the Fort Washington ridge. A few intrepid Dutch farmers established boweries in the Harlem plain during the seventeenth century. The Fort Washington heights were then still a dense forest inhabited by Indians and wolves. The wolves were exterminated from Manhattan by the fearful settlers in 1686, and the Indians met a similar fate when they were finally forced to abandon their last ancestral stronghold on the island in 1715.

The woods were full of all sorts of fur-bearing animals, which provided a lucrative livelihood to members of the Dutch West India Company. Describing the profitable arrangement that had been worked out, Denton said, "The Inhabitants . . . have a considerable Trade with the Indians, for Beavers, Otter, Raccoon skins, with other Furrs; As also for Bear, Deer and Elke skins; and are supplied with Venison and Fowl in the Winter, and Fish in the summer by the Indians which they buy at an easie rate." East Harlem was known by the Dutch as Otterspoor because of the many otters along its sandy stream banks.

Of birds the Dutch patroon David Piertsz DeVries numbered wintering geese "by the thousands" and wild turkeys ranging in weight from "thirty and thirty-six pounds to fifty pounds." Other edible fowl included partridges, meadow hens, white and gray herons and passenger pigeons so thick in migration that "the light can hardly be discerned where they fly."

The waters were as abundantly filled with fish as the skies with birds. In those days before water pollution made New York Harbor a biologically sterile sewer, Danckaerts wrote, "It is not possible to describe how this bay swarms with fish, both large and small, whales, tunnies and porpoises, whole schools of innumerable other fish, which the eagles and other birds of prey swiftly seize in their talons when the fish come to the surface."

The eagles are gone now, and commercial fishing has long since been abandoned in New York Harbor. Indeed, New York seems far removed from that Arcadian time when Danckaerts and his friend Sluyter "walked awhile in the pure morning air, along the margin of the clear running water of the sea, which is driven up the river at every tide."

Still, there are portions of the heritage yet intact, and, what is more, the promise of rapid and spontaneous recovery wherever nature is given a chance. The opportunities for reconstructing ecosystems within the city, or further obliterating them, are at hand. The realization or defeat of these opportunities lies within the realm of politics and public demand.

2

THE FOUNDATIONS

Where wast thou when I laid the foundations of the earth?
. . . Whereupon are the foundations thereof fastened? or
who laid the cornerstone thereof; . . . Or who shut up the
sea with doors, when it brake forth, as if it had issued out of
the womb?

Book of Job

Long before New York became real estate, divided and occupied in accordance with the dictates of men's politics and fortunes, long before it became imprinted with the life-styles of European men, long before man himself even existed, there were the land and the sea. And as the New York of real estate and architecture is dynamic and volatile, a city constantly erasing and rebuilding itself, so, too, on a different time scale, measured in millennia rather than years, the New York of bedrock and water is mobile, changing, with land and sea often alternating roles, responding to the forces of geology and climate. That this process is ongoing, that someday the Chase Manhattan Bank and the Empire State Building may be drowned under hundreds of feet of seawater or their steel and stone moltenly metamorphosed into some future composition of bedrock seems fantastic and inconceivable. But that is only because we accord so much permanence to our own infinitesimal second on the great geologic clock, not comprehending that the only real permanence is change.

The most recent topographical configuration of New York City, the one we know presently, is essentially the product of two forces: an ancient mountain revolution and a relatively recent (in the geologic sense) period of glaciation. According to New York area geologist Christopher J. Schuberth of the American Museum of Natural History, in his book *The Geology of New York City and Environs* (Garden City, New York: Natural History Press, 1968), over 400 million years ago lofty peaks of alpine proportions stood where New York is today. The tremendous heat and pressure which produced this ancient mountain chain caused the sedimentary rocks beneath the earth's surface — shales and limestones — to be severely metamorphosed into formations of gneiss and schist and marble. These shales and limestones were the solidified deposits of mud and seawater precipitates that were laid down nearly 300 million years before the mountain-building event, or 700 million years ago, when the piece of geography represented by New York City lay at the bottom of the sea. During the period of crustal uplift and instability these old sedimentary rocks, which had subsided under the weight of thousands of feet of subsequent sedimentation, became a highly plastic, fluid mass capable of chemical change and formation of new minerals, minerals conspicuously larger in size than those contained in the parent rocks.

New York City's bedrock is composed of three such sedimentary layers recrystallized into tougher, more coursely grained metamorphic stone. As eons of time passed, the towering mountain peaks which were composed of the uptilted strata of the successive periods of sedimentation were worn away by the slow process of erosion. As they were whittled down to stumps the old highly metamorphosed formations with which we are familiar today came to light.

The most ancient of these bedrock strata is called Fordham gneiss (pronounced *nice*). An extremely contorted metamorphosed sandstone characterized by wavy black and white bands, it is the underlying bedrock of the New York City area. Surface exposures of it appear mainly in the Bronx. A first, durable stone, resistant to erosion, it forms an elevated ridge in Riverdale; such names as Fordham Heights, Morris Heights and Highbridge reflect its prominent elevation immediately to the east, where another two-pronged ridge is found. This gneiss formation slopes downward into the earth at a southeasterly angle, making its final surface ap-

Exposed surface of Inwood marble, Isham Park, Manhattan.

pearance in Astoria, Queens. Welfare Island in the East River is a spit of Fordham gneiss. In the last century the stone was quarried on the island by convict labor and used to build the now demolished gray, fortresslike prison, the almshouse, and several hospitals, some of whose ruins can still be seen today.

The rock formation lying on top of the Fordham gneiss is called Inwood marble and takes its name from the Inwood section of Manhattan, where it can be seen in a few exposed surfaces. Because the Inwood marble is a soft stone it is easily eroded. It is natural, therefore, that the Harlem and Hudson rivers cut their beds into the marble rather than the more resistant neighboring gneiss. Many of the valleys and the plains of Manhattan and the Bronx also rest upon Inwood marble. Inwood marble comprises the flat apron that spreads out beneath Inwood Hill in Manhattan. Marble also forms the subsurface of the broad, flat shoulder of northeastern Manhattan upon which Harlem rests. In colonial times both of these plains were covered with extensive salt marshes.

In several places between the "heights" of tougher, less erodable stone are long, continuous bands of Inwood marble. These marble valleys were the most accessible transportation routes in the early days, and in time they became the city's major thoroughfares: Broadway in Manhattan and its continuation in the Bronx, and Jerome, Webster and Tremont avenues in the Bronx — all are underlaid with ribbons of the soft white stone.

The youngest formation is called Manhattan schist, and it is this firm bedrock that supports the city's towering skyscrapers. The division of Manhattan into two zones of tall buildings — downtown and midtown — is not accidental. South of Thirtieth Street the bedrock dips down several feet beneath the earth's surface, but it is still accessible for building foundations until it reaches the north side of Washington Square, where it plunges down below one hundred feet. Greenwich Village and the loft district to the south form the "valley," a region of low buildings set on top of glacial sediments and artificial landfill. Near Chambers Street the schist comes back to within fewer than one hundred feet of street level, giving sufficient anchor to the towers of the financial district. The zoning code of Manhattan is thus written as much by geology as by city planners.

One hundred and twenty million years after the initial period of rock metamorphosis during which the Fordham gneiss, Inwood marble and

Manhattan schist were formed, a second period of crustal instability occurred, allowing injections of granite and granite pegmatite to permeate the existing formations. These injections can be seen as long, light-colored crystalline bands, called sills, paralleling the stratification of the host rock, or as vertical intrusions, called dikes. They are of igneous origin — that is, they are made up of mineral crystallized out of the hot magma that was squirted into the fissures formed when the older rocks were again subjected to heating and pressure within the earth.

The granite pegmatites resemble ordinary granite except that they have visibly larger mineral grains. The large grains indicate a slow cooling process; in some cases granite pegmatites are studded with mineral crystals — garnets, tourmalines, beryl and other semiprecious stones. Manhattan has been a particularly rich mine for mineralogists. According to Dr. Schuberth, the continuous and extensive excavation of its bedrock has yielded over one hundred seventy of the earth's two thousand known minerals, many of spectacular size and quite a few of gem quality. Most of these have come from pegmatitic granite intrusions. A visitor to the fourth floor of the American Museum of Natural History can inspect such collector's items as a ten-pound garnet crystal found at Broadway and Thirty-fifth Street and a sheared chrysoberyl crystal discovered at Riverside Drive and Ninety-third Street, considered to be the finest ever found in North America.

In addition to the granite and granite pegmatite sills and dikes another igneous rock is found in New York City — the Staten Island serpentine, which forms the hilly spine running down the island's center. Capping the serpentine ridge is Todt Hill, 410 feet above sea level, the highest landmark along the entire eastern coastline south of Massachusetts. The serpentine, like the metamorphic rocks discussed above, has undergone alteration by intense heating far below the earth's surface. Unlike them, it was in its premetamorphic state an igneous rather than a sedimentary stone.

The infusion of granitic intrusions into the original bedrock occurred 360 million years ago. At this time the bedrock strata still lay far beneath the earth's surface, submerged under the crushing weight of the mountains above them. But as the mountains eroded away into the sea and the pressure of their load was removed, the metamorphic rocks at their core responded by slowly rising until, shorn of the mighty crests above them,

*Taylor and Skinner map 1781, showing high bedrock ridges of
northern Manhattan and the Bronx, terminal moraine of the
glacier and the swampy outwash plain around Jamaica Bay.*

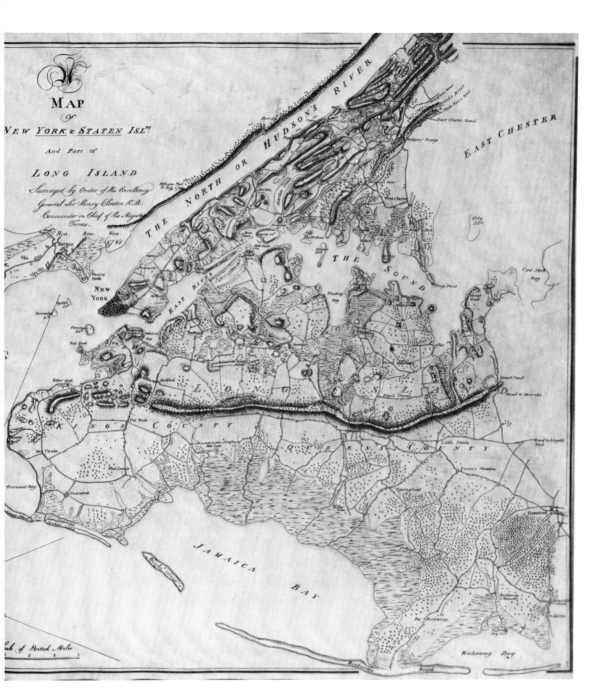

MAP
of
NEW YORK & STATEN ISL^ds.
And Part of
LONG ISLAND
Surveyed by Order of His Excellency
General Sir Henry Clinton K.B.
Commander in Chief of His Majestys
Forces.
&ca. &ca. &ca. 1781

THE NORTH OR HUDSON'S RIVER

EAST CHESTER

THE SOUND

EAST RIVER

NEW YORK

Bergen

L O N G   I S L A ^d.

K I N G S   C O U N T Y

Q U E E N S   C O U N T Y

Hampstead

Springfield

JAMAICA   BAY

Rockaway   Bay

Scale of British Miles

their surfaces exposed, they assumed approximately the position they hold today. Geologists fix the date of the surface exposure of the New York City rock formations at about 190 million years ago.

During the succeeding eons there were periods when the ocean advanced and then retreated and sedimentary deposits were laid down. Subsequent earth movements shoved these sedimentary deposits into yet new mountains and fractured the old bedrock formations beneath them, creating what geologists call fault zones. Again erosion whittled away almost all of the sedimentary strata, leaving, except for a few traces, only the old metamorphic gneiss and marble and schist.

The fault valleys remained, however, and can still be recognized today. Trending in a generally east-west direction (unlike the longitudinal valleys of Inwood marble), these flat, low-lying valleys were the old stream beds discussed in the previous chapter, which were later converted into major crosstown streets. At the northern end of Manhattan the Dyckman Street fault bisects the Fort Washington ridge of Manhattan schist, separating Fort Tryon Park and the Cloisters from Inwood Hill Park. A little farther south 155th Street is aligned along another fault zone. The deepest and most conspicuous of the fault valleys extends from the Hudson River across 125th Street, bending diagonally south to enter the East River at Ninety-sixth Street. Following Broadway from Seventy-second Street to Columbus Circle, another fault zone continues south to enter the East River at Twenty-third Street.

With the positioning of the ancient metamorphic mountain stumps, their subsequent cracking into fault zones, and the erasure of most of the sedimentary deposits from their surfaces, the stage was set for a new act in New York City's long and continuing geologic drama: the age of glaciation. In all, four huge ice sheets pushed down from the north to cover portions of Europe and North America. The last and most important of these movements, and the one whose evidence is imprinted on the landscape of the modern city, was the Wisconsin advance, which began about seventy-five thousand years ago, a mere yesterday on the geologic clock.

As the earth's climate became colder, winters lengthened and accumulated snows were packed into a frozen ice mass. At an estimated rate of a foot a day the great ice sheet moved ponderously southward. Conglomerated fragments of soil and rock were shoved along its undersurface,

22

Glacial pond, Alley Park, Queens.

scraping and polishing the ancient bedrock. Today glacial striations — grooves running in a northeast-to-southwest pattern — mark its passage over exposed outcroppings of many rock surfaces in New York City. Finally, some seventeen thousand years ago the ice became stabilized, with its southern edge tracing a line across the central spine of Long Island and the greater part of Staten Island. Manhattan and the Bronx at this time lay deeply buried under a thousand feet of ice and frozen glacial debris.

But as the winters became warmer, the ice sheet retreated and its meltwaters deposited the fragments uprooted by its advance. These fragments, known as glacial till, were most heavily concentrated along the glacial perimeter in a terminal moraine. This accounts for the protective constriction of the Narrows, where the moraine crossed New York Bay, and for the hilly nature of Staten Island and northern Brooklyn and Queens. The postglacial landscape of these portions of New York are what the geologists call knob and kettle country — a series of depressions alternating with low, moundlike hills. The depressed areas, which are often boggy or water-filled, are kettleholes formed by fragments of ice trapped in the moraine. As the ice melted, the ground level subsided, creating basins of varying dimensions. Lakes and ponds were formed as these basins became containers for melted glacial ice and rainwater. All are shrunken from their original size, for as the land became once again covered by green and living things, plants encroached upon their still waters, and year by year leaves and eroded debris from the surrounding slopes have continued to layer their depths with sedimentary deposits.

Other evidence of glacial visitation is found in the form of large boulders, or erratics, which can be seen in all five boroughs. The often precariously perched erratics of Central Park and the New York Botanical Garden in the Bronx are for the most part chunks of igneous diabase plucked by the glacier from the New Jersey Palisades or metamorphic rock from the Hudson Highlands. Elsewhere, on Long Island, erratics more frequently resemble the metamorphic rocks of Connecticut origin.

The unglaciated portions of New York City — the southern tip of Staten Island and southern Brooklyn and Queens — became part of a vast outwash plain. Carried by the coursing glacial meltwaters, deposits of sand and gravel spread out to form the flat alluvial landscape that reminded the early Dutch settlers of Holland. Postglacial movements of

Rocky coastline, Pelham Bay.

morainal sands from east to west along the Long Island coastline created a chain of barrier beaches. In New York City the Rockaway Peninsula, the barrier beach for Jamaica Bay, continues to push westward an estimated two hundred feet per year, or one mile every twenty-three years.

During the past three hundred years — the last fraction of a second on the geologic clock — man has undoubtedly been the major ecological agent and sculptor of the New York City landscape. He has chopped down forests of trees to make place for a forest of buildings. He has dredged rivers and bays and spanned them with suspension bridges of breathtaking ingenuity. He has filled in marshy inlets and rechanneled streams into a sewerage system. He has blasted away bedrock to create the world's largest network of underground transportation tunnels.

Still, though encrusted with pavements and buildings, the old landforms can be discerned: the gneiss and schist escarpments of the Bronx and Manhattan rearing above the flat valleys and plains of Inwood marble; the rolling morainal hills of northern Brooklyn and Queens; the flat alluvial glacial outwash plain fanning out to embrace Jamaica Bay; the Narrows marking the place where the terminal moraine crossed the harbor leaving an elevated bracket of defense outposts: Fort Hamilton in Brooklyn and Fort Wadsworth on Staten Island; and, protruding here and there from beneath its cover of glacial till, the greenish serpentine, the firm core that pushes Staten Island up out of the sea.

Tantalizing, transitory glimpses of the geology of the city are offered to sidewalk superintendents by new building excavations. For more extended field exploration, there are the parks. In Pelham Bay Park you will find the most southerly segments of the rocky coastline characteristic of New England and eastern Canada. This is a glaciated or "drowned" coast, different in appearance from the mature, alluvial unglaciated barrier beach coastlines of Long Island and New Jersey. The origin of these Pelham Bay rocks is still something of an enigma; geology students attack them with hammers, for they are a fertile subject for doctoral dissertations since their relationship to the rest of the New York City formations is as yet not scientifically established.

In Central Park you can study the bedrock outcroppings of mica schist ribboned with granite intrusions and grooved with glacial scratches that mark the movement of the Wisconsin ice sheet from northeast to southwest some forty thousand years ago. Here and in the New York Botanical Garden you will find those curiously poised erratics left behind when the ice melted.

Morningside Park in Manhattan has a high vertical wall of schist that used to be used by mountain climbers for rock-scaling practice. Inwood Hill Park and Fort Tryon Park, twin elevations of Manhattan schist bisected by the Dyckman Street fault valley, form the northerly extension of the Fort Washington ridge, of which Morningside Park is a part. In Inwood Hill Park you will find glacial potholes, bowl-like depressions scoured out of the bedrock by the gravel-laden meltwaters of the glacier.

Glacial action can be seen also in the rolling terrain of Prospect Park in Brooklyn, which was modeled by the lumpy gravels of the terminal moraine. Kettlehole ponds pocking the moraine are found at High Rock Conservation Center on Staten Island, in Highland Park in Brooklyn and in Alley Park and Forest Park in Queens, a green mantle of duckweed floating on their placid surfaces and skunk cabbages and swamp maples fringing their spongy, peaty borders.

As geology is the city's bones, so botany is its green skin. And, just as there are earth-shaping forces of mountain building and erosion and glaciation that produced the New York topography with which we are familiar, so too there are forces of climate and soil formation and plant succession that produced the New York landscape of forests and wetlands that became the stage upon which the urban drama — and, incidentally, the biological drama — is still being enacted.

Glacial pothole, Inwood Hill Park.

27

3

FORESTS AND WETLANDS

Most of the plant types known today were in existence before the Ice Age. The frozen shield that moved like a monolithic bulldozer across the land killed all the vegetation in its path, but the plants were not exterminated. For the most part they simply reestablished themselves farther south.

According to paleobotanists, below the margin of the glacier there were successive plant zones: a frozen tundra; a tundra mixed with some hardy evergreens; a spruce zone containing stands of birch and pine; a zone of predominantly pine with an admixture of oak and hemlock; and a deciduous forest of oak, hickory and chestnut.

Four times the ice descended from the pole and then withdrew again. During interglacial intervals, as the climate became increasingly warmer, the boundaries of the plant zones shifted northward, but as the crushing load of ice inched its way south once more, they again retreated. The estimated time of the last glacial withdrawal from the New York City area, originally thought to have been eleven thousand years ago, has been recently revised to seventeen thousand years ago by Dr. Leslie A. Sirkin of Adelphi University on the basis of radiocarbon dating of fossil pollen preserved in glacial bogs in the city and on Long Island and in New Jersey.

Glacial advance and retreat caused a corresponding shift in the level of the sea. When the massive ice sheet had accumulated into itself a great deal of the water of the sea, the continental boundaries were expanded and the landmass embraced as much as a hundred miles of what is today the ocean shelf. But as the ice melted, the ocean inundated the coastal plains once more and invaded the mouths of rivers to create deep harbors.

If we could look at the New York landscape since the Ice Age in speeded-up film going backwards we would see its present deciduous forests taking on a progressively northern character until they resembled the tall spruce forests of New England and Canada. Eventually in this hypothetical film the city would be covered by tundra; then, as in Labrador today, there would be only cold, bare, gravelly moraine and gouged and deeply scratched rocks with a few mosses and lichens struggling for a foothold. The present rocky shoreline of the Bronx, which according to Dr. Schuberth did not reach its present transgressive position until five thousand to six thousand years ago, would lie far to the east in Long Island Sound as the imprisonment of a still-great quantity of water in the ice cap kept the sea level down. On Long Island, beneath the margin of the terminal moraine, coursing meltwaters would form braided rivulets; their load of glacial debris would in time build up the flat, sandy outwash plain upon which southern Brooklyn and Queens rest today. There would be no Rockaway Peninsula; it would take many centuries for the westward shifting sands borne by ocean currents to build up the Long Island barrier beaches and to produce the long sheltering arm that would permit the growth of grassy marsh islands in the calm waters of Jamaica Bay.

The salt marshes that we know today in glaciated New York and New England began their formation about four thousand years ago, after the climate had warmed up and the combination of erosion of land sediments and deposition of tide-borne sediments made flat, sandy beds in coves and other areas protected from the force of the beating surf. In these places, in the intertidal zone where seawater mingles with freshwater streams, spartina grass, a plant adapted to just such conditions of semisalinity, began to form a green fringe around the edge of the land. The roots of the spartina grass trapped additional sediments transported inland by the tide; rotting grasses built up the soil, and little by little, aided by a gradually rising sea level, these marsh areas extended themselves. Multibranched, meandering tidal creeks established sinuous irrigation networks through them. In the wetter areas, along the tidal creek banks, the tall cordgrass *Spartina alterniflora* was dominant; the upland marsh, inundated by only the highest tides, was colonized by the short salt meadow grass *Spartina patens*.

Realizing the value of *Spartina patens* as hay for their cattle, the early colonists quickly entered into negotiations with the Indians, who bartered away large portions of their valuable coastal lands and adjacent marshes for the white man's tools and weapons and for his worthless beads and trinkets. In this manner the Canarsie salt meadows bordering Jamaica Bay, which had by the seventeenth century grown to extensive proportions, were acquired from the Canarsie Indians to be held in common by the residents of the little Dutch town of Flatbush. The colonists mowed the hard salt grass with scythes and stacked it on staddles — clustered poles driven into the ground along the edge of the marsh above the high-tide level. Much later the farmers developed horse-drawn mowing machines. Longtime residents of Staten Island can still remember the mowing machines that harvested the abundant salt hay crop in the Fresh Kills meadows.

New findings have been added to the history of postglacial forest development in the New York area by the recent studies of Dr. Sirkin and his associates. Boring into bog basins they have extracted long cores of layered sediments from the bog mat extending down to the bed of coarse glacial gravel on which the bog was formed. By analyzing the stratified pollen grains within the core samples, Dr. Sirkin was able to correlate different forest sequences with various intervals of time in the life of the bog and arrive at the conclusion that there was an early stage of postglacial plant life in the area as far back as seventeen thousand years ago.

In Alley Park in Queens the first plants to put down roots in the sandy sediments adjacent to the bog bottom between seventeen thousand and fifteen thousand years ago were some scrubby pines and small birches.

During the next two thousand years arctic willows and grasses were added, and then spruces and larger pines. A northern type of forest — spruce mixed with pine and fir — stayed in the area until around nine thousand years ago; then during the next two thousand years a forest predominantly of pine appeared; that gave way around seven thousand years ago to a forest of oak and chestnut and hemlock. Between five thousand and two thousand years ago the hemlocks vanished and hickories appeared on the scene. Other species such as holly and birch became mixed with these dominant forest types.

This last stage was essentially the forest that the first European visitors beheld when they sailed into New York Harbor. But the postglacial botanical migration was and still is going on, and the first settlers noticed other species as well that we now know are invaders from the south: sweetgum, tulip tree, persimmon, hackberry, sweetbay magnolia, and willow oak. New York City is in fact particularly interesting to botanists because it marks the border between two plant zones. Not only are there southern trees mixing with the predominantly oak-hickory forest cover, but also trees characteristic of the New England forests farther north: maples, beeches, birches. A northern evergreen, the hemlock, has a rear-guard stand in the New York Botanical Garden. This particular patch of woods has, in addition, the distinction of being the only piece of virgin forest intact and unmodified in the five boroughs.

The native forest that Van der Donck thought so limitless was not long in being cut down. He spoke of the quality of that timber, oak trees "from sixty to seventy feet high without knots, and from two to three fathoms thick, being of various sizes." DeVries mentioned the fir trees in what is now the Kingsbridge section of the Bronx, saying. "We generally had fine masts from there." Encamping Tory and Hessian forces chopped down large areas of the city's forests for firewood during Revolutionary times.

Some trees have been exterminated from the area. The once prevalent cedars of Long Island and Staten Island have succumbed to urbanization and air pollution. Walnut trees, prized by cabinetmakers and manufacturers of gunstocks, have all but disappeared. The noble chestnut, remarked in the botanical records of all the colonial journalists, was a dominant forest tree in the New York range. But it had disappeared by the

Sweetgum leaves, Alley Park, Queens.

early years of this century, a victim of a fungus accidentally imported from Asia. It is a prolific sprouter; new shoots can still be seen growing from old stumps. (I have seen such a sprouting chestnut stump at High Rock Conservation Center on Staten Island.) However, as a great New York City naturalist, John Kieran, has poignantly pointed out, these sprouts are the Peter Pans of the tree world, destined never to grow up, for they too must become infected by the fatal fungus. A similar sad end now appears to be overtaking the American elm, which once arched its graceful branches over so many New York City streets, as scientists continue to search for a cure to the Dutch elm disease.

The native vegetation was, of course, supplemented by many new varieties which the settlers brought as seeds, slips and roots from their homelands. The importation of foreign plant species did not begin in earnest, however, until the early eighteenth century, with the establishment of America's first commercial nurseries around Flushing. Besides having their agents scour Europe for new plants, the early nurserymen commissioned ship captains to bring back seeds and slips from Japan and China. Today an estimated forty per cent of the New York City plant life is of European origin.

The Flushing nurseries continued a thriving business through the nineteenth century as their specimen collections of such exotics as the Lombardy poplar, cedar of Lebanon, pawlonia, copper beech, Japanese maple, Chinese larch and a variety of magnolias were transferred to estates and public parks. Kissena Park in Queens is itself the site of a famous old nursery and contains many botanical rarities. In now-wild park areas that are the sites of former estates, such as the Inwood Hill ridge in Manhattan and Hunter's Island in Pelham Bay Park, these stately specimen trees stand like distinguished foreign dignitaries at a reception while the home-bred species of the second-growth forest, eager to pay their respects, shoulder up around them.

Today most New York City street trees are non-natives, oriental species or hybrids combining foreign and domestic strains. The ginkgo or maidenhair tree, an import from China recognized by its queer, butterfly-shaped leaf, is a successful street tree because of its straight-upward branching habit. As its atavistic appearance suggests, it is the oldest known tree, a survivor from the period of the dinosaurs. It is also an extremely healthy

34

The largest tulip tree on Long Island, Alley Park.

tree, seldom infected by insects or fungi, which perhaps explains its longevity as a species.

The ubiquitous London plane tree, characterized by its pale, mottled trunk and globular seedcases that dangle like Christmas balls on its bare winter branches, is a hybrid combining the American sycamore and the oriental sycamore. Along the shoreline of the Narrows and beside the Belt Parkway in southern Brooklyn the salt air–tolerant Russian olive and Japanese black pine are planted. Another oriental import, the ailanthus, misnamed the tree of heaven, is the city's number one weed tree; it is foulodored and springs up everywhere, particularly in vacant lots.

While the story of the city's forests is one of change and modification, the story of its wetlands is one of progressive annihilation. By 1900 the once extensive Manhattan marshes, with the exception of some fragments at the northern end totaling less than one square mile, had been filled in and built over. Still, in 1900 there were large stretches of marshland totaling 42.5 square miles in the other boroughs, most notably around Jamaica Bay and the southern end of Staten Island. Today only 6.4 square miles of unfilled marshes remain.

As an increasing population began to press upon the city's diminishing land supply, it became increasingly profitable to reclaim marshes with landfill high enough to resist tidal inundation and firm enough to support buildings. Today Co-op City in the East Bronx rests upon a sandy slurry pumped out of Eastchester Bay and piped to a former marsh. LaGuardia Airport, Shea Stadium and the World's Fair grounds have replaced the Flushing salt meadows. Kennedy Airport was built upon stabilized Jamaica Bay marshlands.

"Landfill," when preceded by the word "sanitary," is a euphemism for "garbage dump," and the topography of marshes — low-lying, level, treeless — makes them ideal municipal dumps, besides which, they often are already in the public domain. In the city of New York there are in any one year nearly two hundred acres of sanitary landfill in operation. At present the largest landfill site is at Fresh Kills on Staten Island, a three-thousand-acre refuse heap created over the past thirty years, to which nearly ten thousand tons of garbage are now barged every day.

Commonly considered useless lands, marshes are in reality uncommonly useful. They are natural floodplains absorbing the runoff from heavy rainfalls, and buffer zones dissipating the force of waves caused by storms at sea. To replace them with flood control devices is costly. The destruction and building over of the marshes of southern Brooklyn and Queens has resulted in an all too common environmental irony — in this case, a proposal by the Army Corps of Engineers to construct a $55.5 million hurricane barrier at the mouth of Jamaica Bay. In addition, the nutrient-rich waters of marshes are spawning and nursery grounds for many fish and shellfish. The combined effects of water pollution and marsh destruction have completely eliminated the city's once profitable fishing industry.

The remnants of New York City's once luxurious mantle of marshlands are prolific laboratories for the naturalist in spite of the urbanization all around them. So, too, the city's natural history is written in its forests in splendid, seasonal letters, bold and large enough to be read still. New York's forests and wetlands tell more than simply a story of nature; they tell a story of man and his power to shape and alter, to destroy and, sometimes, to remake the natural world.

Boating on the tidal creeks of Fresh Kills marsh, 1896.

The site of Fresh Kills marsh today.

4

THE CAMPFIRES

OF INWOOD HILL

Paralleling the Henry Hudson Parkway near the northern end of Manhattan is a towering escarpment some two hundred feet high, the Fort Washington ridge — an extended outcropping of the tough, resistant bedrock, Manhattan schist. At the parkway toll bridge the schist abruptly breaks off, dropping steeply into the waters of Spuyten Duyvil Creek, which connects the Hudson and Harlem rivers and separates Manhattan from the Bronx mainland. Here, its most northerly point, the Fort Washington ridge is called Inwood Hill. From its wooded crest you can look across to the New Jersey Palisades and up the broad sweep of the Hudson, its powerful current alternating direction with the changing tides.

Acquisition of Inwood Hill for a park was first proposed in 1895. At that time the city administration was deaf to the suggestion of financing a park in such a remote and semirural area. Industrial development was considered instead. Plans were advanced for creating a port of call along the Hudson between Dyckman Street and Spuyten Duyvil Creek. In 1912 the lovely northern tip of the hill was sold to a private dock company, which announced that "the work of clearing the hill of timber will soon be underway, and ground will be broken for the construction of the docks and warehouses in the spring." Luckily, neither the shoreline nor the hilltop disfigurement occurred, and the property fell into the hands of a land speculator who hoped to profit by the sale of lots when Riverside Drive was extended north.

With sentiment rising for the park, particularly as certain archaeological discoveries began to illuminate the historical importance of the area, the owner made a formal offer of sale to the city on April 22, 1914. After a series of resolutions approved by the Board of Estimate the city map was changed: Riverside Drive was redrawn to its present terminus at Dyckman Street, and Inwood Hill and its surrounding lowland were officially designated a park May 29, 1916.

Unlike adjacent Fort Tryon Park, which has been extensively landscaped, Inwood Hill Park still has a wilderness character. There have been but few major improvements. In 1967 lighting was installed along the pathways winding back and forth across the hillside, a source of disgust to many park frequenters, who feel that the lights introduce an alien note into the landscape. The paths themselves are a legacy of the WPA days in the 1930's. In 1968 a nature trail was laid out, but unfortunately, its informational markers were soon vandalized. Some selective forestry is conducted by a troop of Boy Scouts working under Parks Department supervision; the scouts position dead trees to control soil erosion and as cribbing for the steep hillside pathways.

The Inwood forest consists mainly of deciduous trees, although a few hemlocks stand out greenly against the bare branches of winter. Native trees include six species of maple and five of oak. There are hackberries and black cherries, birches and hickories. Huge tulip trees with columnar trunks rise fifty or more feet. There are a grove of black locusts, whiteflowered in summer, and a stand of Osage orange trees with wood so hard that Indians once used it for their arrows, and policemen once did for their nightsticks. Its thorny branches make an impenetrable haven for small birds, while its queer, convoluted fruit is sometimes likened to the human brain. On top of the ridge, beside the meadow upon which used to be the

42

Tulip trees in a snowstorm, Inwood Hill Park.

House of Mercy, a home for delinquent girls, are three immense eastern cottonwoods.

Besides its native trees, the park has some majestic specimen imports which date from one hundred to one hundred fifty years ago, when private estates dotted the ridge overlooking the Hudson. These include a copper beech with a girth of over thirteen feet and a ginkgo so venerable that it must have been one of the first of that species imported from the Far East in the early nineteenth century. Inwood's arboreal showpiece is gone, however; it was a tulip tree at the foot of the hill estimated to be over two hundred fifty years old and hailed as the oldest living thing on Manhattan Island when it became damaged in the hurricane of 1938.

The main shrub of the Inwood forest is the fragrant-leaved spicebush, which flowers brilliant yellow in the early spring. As the days grow warmer wildflowers appear: jack-in-the-pulpit and what is probably the last remaining patch of mayapple on Manhattan. Tall grasses shelter nesting pheasants. Recently a red fox was seen in the park and black squirrels as well as the common gray. A few years back muskrats swam along the banks of Spuyten Duyvil Creek; not long ago wild swans came to the creek, too. The black-crowned night herons are gone since the destruction of their favorite cattail swamp, but green herons can still be spotted beside Spuyten Duyvil Creek.

The best place for bird watching is in the Clove, a valley splitting the Inwood escarpment into two steep-sided prongs. Much of the erosion which created the valley was accomplished during the last ice age by the meltwaters of the receding glacier. Potholes, bowl-like depressions scoured into the cliff face by the swirling glacial gravels, can be seen along the West Ridge where it bends to form a "canoe prow." In the sheltered recesses of the Clove there are titmice and vireos, cardinals and grosbeaks, and in the spring and fall a myriad of migrating warblers. The Clove is also the site of the last traces of Indian occupation on Manhattan.

The first discovery of aboriginal remains occurred in 1890 when three archaeology buffs began exploring the area. Where the Clove opened out into a broad salt marsh (now covered over by ball fields) a cold spring gushed out of the earth. This spring, in colonial times referred to as "the fonteyn against the high land," discharged an estimated six gallons a min-

Tulip tree which used to be at Inwood Hill Park, considered to be the oldest living thing on Manhattan Island before its destruction in 1939.

Jack-in-the-pulpit, Inwood Hill Park.

Mayapple blossom, Inwood Hill Park.

ute and was reputed to be the largest within New York City. Later during the era of the WPA its waters were forced into a pipe; today the runoff from the spring flows through a culvert into Spuyten Duyvil Creek.

The origin of the name "Spuyten Duyvil" remains something of a mystery. Washington Irving created a legendary explanation when he described the determined Dutchman who vowed to swim across the stream at high tide "in spite of the devil." More likely, "spuyten" refers to the spouting spring below Inwood Hill, and "duyvil" is a misspelling of *duyvel,* the Dutch word for meadow — in this case, the salt meadow through which the spouting spring flowed.

A copious water supply, protection from winter winds in the deep sheltering valley, and access to the fishing grounds of the Hudson and East rivers made the area ideally suited for Indian settlement. So reasoned the archaeologists. Probing in the dry bed of the old stream that once ran through the bottom of the Clove, they discovered three large refuse heaps containing oyster shells, animal bones and pipe fragments. Then one of the men noticed some large overhanging rocks embedded in the hillside. As he dug away the dirt and forest debris in front of the rocks he found the entrance to a small cave chamber. With mounting excitement he began to turn the soft earth of the cave floor with his trowel, uncovering many large pottery shards. According to a newspaper report of the day, "after six hours of digging Mr. Chenoweth had all the fragments of six pots of curious forms and unique manufacture." On the following day as he again dug the cave floor he discovered an entrance leading into a second chamber, the size of which caused him to conclude "that it was the main room of a cavernous retreat." In it he found a rude fireplace; light gleamed through a chimney crevice in the rocks overhead.

In addition to this cave, which was probably formed when frost and glacial meltwaters loosened rock slabs from the cliff face causing them to collapse into the side of the hill, there were two other caves. One was a crevice at the foot of the cliff, another an excavation under a large fallen fragment.

The archaeologists' discoveries, now housed in the American Museum of Natural History, are relics of the Wick-quas-keeks, a branch of the Wapanachi (or Wappinger) tribe, members of the Mohican group of the Algonquin nation. The Wick-quas-keeks occupied northern Manhattan,

47

the Bronx and part of Westchester. Their headquarters were at Dobbs Ferry. The Manhattan group of Wick-quas-keeks were known as Rech-ga-wa-wancs after their sachem Rechgawac, whose chieftaincy lasted from around 1639 to 1669. Rechgawac had his headquarters at what is now Park Avenue and Ninety-fourth Street, and the Wick-quas-keek domain extended south to somewhere around Fifty-ninth Street. Across the creek opposite Inwood Hill on Spuyten Duyvil Hill (whose rock face is today painted with a huge blue C for Columbia to encourage the home team at Baker Field) was a large village called Nipinisicken. The area along the banks of Spuyten Duyvil Creek was known as Shorakapkok, variously translated as "the sitting down and resting place" and "the wet ground place."

The Wick-quas-keeks were a squat people. Each male wore a long forelock hanging to one side of his head and shaved off the rest of his hair with the exception of a bristling coxcomb on top. They painted their faces in a fiendish manner, declaring they were the *mannette* (devil) personified. Their clothes were fashioned out of turkey feathers and animal hides. Friendly promiscuity and instant divorce characterized their tribal mores. The outcome of courtship was determined by which brave could give the most *zeewan* (shell money) to a prospective bride.

The Wick-quas-keeks were fond of dancing and feasts. For food they usually had abundant game — deer, turkey, rabbit, even bear and wildcat — and plentiful fish and oysters. According to one early journalist they also ate "badgers, dogs, eagles and similar trash, which Christians in no way regard," along with "snakes, frogs, and such like, which they usually cook with offals and entrails." Beans and corn were cultivated, these Mesoamerican staples having gradually been carried north through a chain of intertribal seed gifts. They were planted in such a manner that the cornstalks acted as climbing poles for the bean vines. When the corn was harvested, it was dried and then pounded and mixed with water to form *sapaen,* a mush dish which accompanied most meals and sometimes served as a meal in itself.

The Wick-quas-keeks were among the first Indians of North America to glimpse the astonishing sight of European sailors. In 1609 the Englishman Henry Hudson sailed the Dutch vessel *Half Moon* into the mouth of the great North River, which was later renamed for him. The crew proceeded

49

The "Clove," Inwood Hill Park.

The Indian caves at Inwood Hill Park.

upstream to Albany, where shallow waters forced them to turn around. The ship was met all along the way by natives eager to barter tobacco and corn for the white man's knives and beads. When a canoe filled with Wick-quas-keeks rowed out to meet the *Half Moon* as it put in near Spuyten Duyvil, the crew managed to capture two Indians, probably with the intention of taking them back to Europe for display as curiosities. The Indians later escaped, one drowning in the process. The survivor made his way back to Nipinisicken, where a war council was held. When Hudson and his men returned to the mouth of Spuyten Duyvil on October 2, two canoes full of angry Wick-quas-keeks attacked them with bows and arrows. A cannon shot from the ship dispatched two Indians. The rest quickly returned to shore and fled into the Inwood forest. A third canoe bravely ventured out, and one more Indian was killed by a cannon shot. Hudson's men then fired their muskets, killing an additional three or four.

50

With this parting salvo the strange invaders set sail for home, and the Wick-quas-keeks had only their Indian neighbors to quarrel with for the next few years.

The early explorers had not missed observing that the Indians clothed themselves in beaver pelts and deerskins and "divers sorts of good furres." They brought back to Amsterdam the news of forests and streams filled with mink, muskrat, otter, beaver, fox. In 1621 the Dutch West India Company was authorized to capitalize on the lucrative New World fur trade. The company financed the foundation of trading colonies at Fort Orange (now Albany) and Fort Amsterdam. Peter Minuit was appointed director of Fort Amsterdam. In 1625 he negotiated his famous transaction, purchasing Manhattan Island for twenty-four dollars' worth of beads and trinkets. The historic sale is now believed to have occurred not at Fort Amsterdam, near the island's southern tip, but rather somewhere near the cold spring at Inwood Hill.

However the Dutch may have interpreted the terms of the agreement, the Wick-quas-keeks felt no obligation to relinquish their portion of Manhattan extending north of Rechgawac's (Harlem) Creek, which emptied into the East River at what is now 107th Street. Indeed, during the first few years when the little settlement consisted of a few wooden houses huddled around the fort at the southern tip of the island, the question was purely academic. Later, as the Dutch wished to extend their boweries northward, it became necessary to enter into a series of new treaties and purchases; and it was not until 1715 that the Indians were finally expelled from their last Manhattan retreat, Inwood Hill.

The relationship of the Indians and the settlers, soothed by the force of some mutual economic benefit and abetted by the disposition of the Dutch men toward the Indian women, soon degenerated. The man most responsible for the sorry outcome was William Kieft, who was appointed director of Fort Amsterdam in 1638, at the same time Rechgawac was assuming leadership of his clan of Wick-quas-keeks. Inept at both business and diplomacy, Kieft chose to memorialize himself with a costly new church while simultaneously using his power as commander of the Fort Amsterdam garrison to perpetrate sadistic acts of murderous barbarity on his Indian neighbors. Minor Indian provocations received hostile reprisals out of all proportion to the crimes committed, and the Indians not unex-

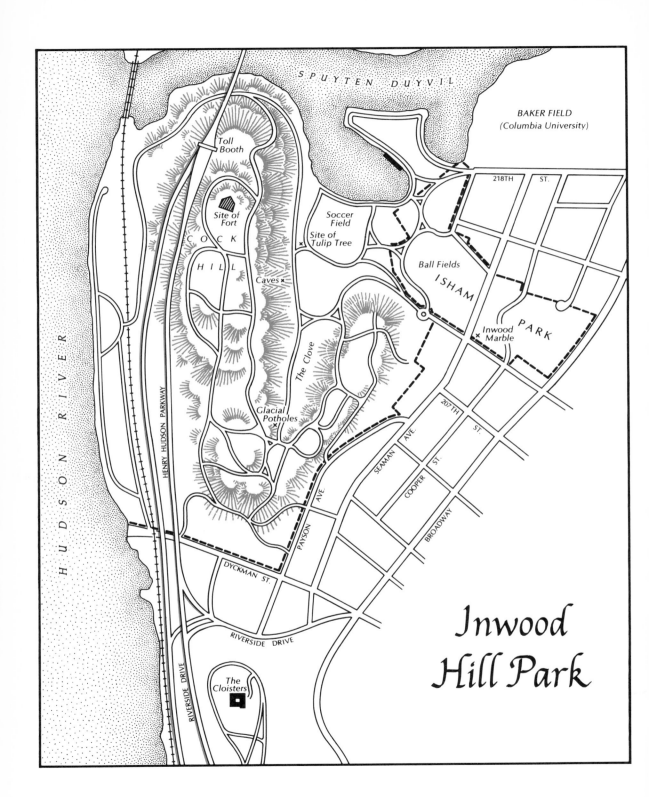

SPUYTEN DUYVIL

BAKER FIELD
(Columbia University)

Toll
Booth

Site of Fort

COCK

HILL

Soccer
Field
Site of
Tulip Tree

Ball Fields

ISHAM

PARK

Caves

Inwood
Marble

H U D S O N   R I V E R

The Clove

Glacial
Potholes

218TH   ST.

207TH

ST.

SEAMAN

AVE.

COOPER

ST.

PAYSON

AVE.

BROADWAY

HENRY HUDSON PARKWAY

DYCKMAN   ST.

RIVERSIDE DRIVE

RIVERSIDE DRIVE

The
Cloisters

*Inwood
Hill Park*

pectedly avenged themselves by killing several settlers. A further annoyance to the Indians was the corn tax, which Kieft stubbornly determined to levy on them. According to the patroon DeVries the Indians "were very much surprised that the Sachem, who was now at the Fort dare exact it; and he must be a very mean fellow to come to this country without being invited by them, and now compel them to give him their corn for nothing."

On February 22, 1643, the Wick-quas-keeks were attacked by the Mohawk Indians from the north. When the Wick-quas-keeks fled from Inwood Hill to Pavonia — across the Hudson from Fort Amsterdam on the New Jersey shore — Kieft, who had been eager for some time to "wipe the mouths of the Indians," saw that his opportunity was at hand. On the night of February 25, soldiers from the fort under orders from Kieft rowed across to the Indians' encampment, where they indulged in an orgy of carnage and torture. DeVries, who had pleaded that the troops not be sent, kept watch back at the fort, from which he could hear the terrified screams of the victims. By his account, "infants were torn from their mothers' breasts, and hacked to pieces in the presence of the parents, and the pieces thrown into the fire and in the water . . . and other sucklings were bound to small boards, then cut, stuck, and pierced, and miserably massacred." The survivors of the ordeal later appeared "with their hands, some with their legs cut off, and some holding their entrails in their arms, and others had such horrible cuts and gashes, that worse than they were could never happen." The same night another contingent of soldiers massacred eighty more Indians encamped at Corlear's Hook. Upon their return, DeVries comments, the soldiers were treated as if "they had done a deed of Roman valor," and "Director Kieft thanked them by taking them by the hand and congratulating them."

The Indians, when they discovered that the massacre had been perpetrated not by a party of other Indians but by the Dutch, promptly revenged themselves by looting and burning every farm and killing all the men they could find. Kieft finally negotiated a temporary peace by buying off Rechgawac and the other offended sachems with presents. His gifts must not have been magnanimous, for the Indians went away grumbling that "it might fall out that the infants upon the small boards would be remembered."

Indian harassment continued as the beleaguered settlers petitioned Amsterdam for Kieft's replacement. Finally a peace treaty was concluded in August 1645; in 1648 Kieft was replaced by robust, peg-legged, peppery Peter Stuyvesant. Stuyvesant's administration, which lasted until the British takeover in 1664, was as troubled as Kieft's. The Dutch farmers had from the beginning been scattered across the countryside, not clustered in villages like the English, and this made them more vulnerable to attack. As Stuyvesant continued to issue patents to Wick-quas-keek lands, tension and insecurity mounted. In 1655 a war party assembled at Inwood Hill for the purpose of raiding Fort Amsterdam. Repelled from that stronghold, the Indians pillaged the outpost farms, massacring the men and carrying into captivity more than a hundred women and children. The captives were eventually returned for ransom, and an ordinance was issued forbidding further settlement of the outlying lands.

In 1658, the settlers, encouraged by an interlude of peace, again ventured into the northern Manhattan hinterland. This time, however, they adopted the English model and founded a town — Nieu Haarlem. Their town's charter, as reissued by Governor Nicolls after the British ouster of the Dutch, included all of the island north of a line following streams and other prominent landscape features from what is today Seventy-fourth Street and the East River to 130th Street and the Hudson.

Although the Wick-quas-keeks were compensated upon various occasions in the usual manner with tools and trinkets, it was never entirely clear to them that they were supposed to relinquish their claim to northern Manhattan. Though mainly encamped in the wilds of Rockland County, they still kept reasserting hunting and fishing rights to their ancestral lands around Inwood Hill. Then in 1675, the English governor, fearing the Wick-quas-keeks might join the rebellion of the New England Indians, invited them back to spend the winter at Wicker's Creek, a corruption of their name now used to refer to their Inwood Hill retreat. The Indians shrewdly took advantage of the tense situation to ask permission to cultivate their old planting ground near Spuyten Duyvil the following spring.

Permission was granted, but as soon as the New England war was over in 1677, the Spuyten Duyvil lowland was divided up among the freeholders of Nieu Haarlem. The largest tracts went to Jan Dyckman and Jan

Nagel; and where the Indian planting ground had been, an apple and pear orchard was established. The Wick-quas-keeks were forced back to the deep forest that ran along the Fort Washington ridge, whose woods they shared with the wolves. The wolves were exterminated when the settlers of Nieu Haarlem organized a hunt in 1686, and though some Wick-quas-keeks lingered on, it was only a matter of time before a final transaction was arranged, and in 1715 they relinquished, once and for all, any claim to their patrimony. Still, some Indians remained in the area well into the nineteenth century, many of them intermingling with the Negro slaves that labored on the Dyckman and Nagel farms.

For sixty years following the negotiations of 1715, Nagels and Dyckmans farmed the lands that had belonged to the Wick-quas-keeks. The southeast portion of Inwood Hill was part of the extensive Dyckman tract occupying some four hundred acres. The forested northern half was owned by the Nagels, who called the Clove their woodlot. The old Indian trail became first the King's Way, later the Albany Post Road, and finally Broadway. Taverns were opened — the Blue Bell, Morris's White House, the Widow Day's — to serve travelers passing over the King's Bridge between Manhattan and the Bronx.

Then from 1776 until 1783 northern Manhattan was enfolded in the drama of the Revolutionary War. In the beginning the farmhouses were appropriated as staff quarters for the patriot army. As increasing numbers of soldiers streamed into the area, an encampment was established at the foot of Fort Washington ridge. On the heights, with their commanding view of ship movement up and down the Hudson, a chain of fortifications was constructed. On Long Hill, the present site of the Cloisters, were Fort Washington and Fort Tryon. Below to the east on Laurel Hill lay Fort George. Further north on the Inwood cliff was Cock Hill Fort, a five-sided earthwork overlooking Spuyten Duyvil Creek.

"Cock Hill" is thought to derive from the last syllable of "Shora-kapkok," a lingering memory of Indian days. General Washington, writing about his reconnaissance of the area in 1781, remarked, "The fort on Cox's hill was in bad repair, and but little dependence placed upon it." American occupation of the area was brief, for on November 16, 1776, the redoubts and adjacent encampment fell into British and Hessian hands. The victory was executed in large by hired Hessian mercenaries under the

British and Hessian attack on Fort Washington and Inwood Hill, 1776.

command of General Baron Wilhelm von Knyphausen, and Fort Washington was rechristened Fort Knyphausen in his honor.

The men of Hesse-Cassel were the most numerous of the troops rented out to the British by a group of debt-ridden Germanic princes. Marching toward the King's Bridge and Inwood Hill following the Battle of White Plains, they were a ferocious spectacle with their towering brass-fronted caps, tallow-plastered hair braided in waist-length queues, and moustaches dyed with blacking. Their yellow breeches and black cloth gaiters were topped by blue coats crossed with belts whitened by pipe clay. They wore as well bayonet belts and scabbards. Pewter buttons bearing their regimental insignias decorated their coats.

Many of these pewter buttons have been found in Inwood Hill Park along with other relics of the Revolutionary occupation — some fragments of blue-patterned earthenware, old bottles, musket shot, shoe buckles. Such artifacts can be seen in the relic room of the Dyckman House at Broadway and 204th Street. Included in that display is a tooth-marked bullet probably bitten by some anguished soldier undergoing surgery or a beating.

Terrified at the Hessian reputation for brutality, the patriot soldiers at

56

the defeated Fort Washington garrison attempted to ingratiate themselves with the mercenaries by offerings of pressed punch, wine and cold cakes. They were nonetheless forced to march between a double line of Hessian soldiers and lay down their arms before being taken away under heavy guard to the city, where they were thrown into Bridewell Prison.

Although no more fighting occurred on Manhattan for the next seven years, Hessian and British troops used the area around Fort Washington as a military base. The diary of a young Saxon chasseur, Sergeant John Charles Philip von Krafft, details the miseries and deprivations of that occupation.

The soldiers were housed in huts built into the hillside below the fort along what is today Payson Avenue. There were ten men to a hut and nine huts to a company. Plagued with diarrhea and mosquitoes, the men were often on the brink of starvation. On the march they received nothing but salt pork, crackers and rum for rations. Though officially forbidden to pillage nearby farms, they frequently did so. In the fall of 1778, when the hungry soldiers were on the verge of mutiny, they staged a massive raid on the Bronx countryside. Pigs and chickens were slaughtered, and fruit trees were stripped bare. Angry farmers fired muskets as the soldiers returned to camp two abreast, each pair of men carrying the plunder on a stake between them. The feasting was soon over, and after that the scoured land yielded only chestnuts. As winter set in, food was scarce or nonexistent; provision ships coming up the Hudson were frequently icebound or otherwise delayed. Then the soldiers were reduced to a monotonous diet of a "miserable oat-grits bread" which, von Krafft says, "weighed very heavy and with the same weight it lay in our stomachs."

Besides being hungry, the men were often near freezing. Although the huts had large fireplaces and the nearby hills in the beginning of the war were well furnished with wood, "the snow found the smallest crevices in the roof and it lay a hand high right near the fire without melting it." By 1779, the once dense forest had been cut down, and the rain carved muddy gullies in the denuded hillside. Firewood had to be imported from Morrisania. Between bouts of sickness and melancholy von Krafft wrote letters to girls — Miss Weinstockin, his sweetheart back home in Braunsberg, and Madame Follert, a Canadian actress with whom he had fallen madly in love while en route to New York. Stricken with fever that summer, he cried out despairingly in his journal: "I would be glad to die, were it not that I must die a sub-officer (that worries me on account of my relatives, even on the brink of the grave)."

The war had its lighter side as well. Cock Hill Fort, because of its isolated location and the steep climb to reach it, was rarely visited by staff; it was therefore a good spot for gambling and grog parties. There was a large contingent of camp followers including a number of wives. One soldier managed to be married by different English and German chaplains "sixteen times to loose women of the town." He told von Krafft that he hoped to do so often again before making up his mind "to take the last one in real earnest."

With the coming of warm weather the men were able to plant vegetables and so relieve the shortage of fresh food. According to von Krafft's description, the entire hillside between the huts was covered with garden plots. He himself had "two pretty spots" near his hut on which he raised "almost all the necessary vegetables."

As the war drew to a close, desertions among the Hessians were frequent, particularly as the summer heat brought on another epidemic of fever. A gallows was erected in September 1783, from which deserters were hanged in effigy. The punishment for insubordination was running the gauntlet; in one instance a soldier was forced to pass naked between a double line of two hundred men six times as they lashed his backside with the flats of their swords.

After the war was over and the soldiers had evacuated, the Dyckmans and Nagels went about reconstructing their farms. The old Dyckman apple and pear orchard had been cut down to form a barricade between Fort George and Fort Tryon. Inwood Hill lay barren, denuded of timber, dusty in summer, awash with mud in winter. Embedded in the Dyckman portion of the hillside were the remains of the Hessian hut camp.

With back-breaking effort, the Dyckman farm laborers removed the huts, and in the depressions that were left in the earth they planted a new apple orchard. That orchard is gone now. The trees of the present Inwood Hill forest that seem so venerable and indestructible will someday also be replaced by others. Inwood Hill is a powerful reminder of the fecundity of land: that it can embrace so many lives — Wick-quas-keeks, Dutch, patriots, Hessians, farmers, land speculators, the WPA, Boy Scouts — and still, in obedience to the rhythm of the seasons, flourish and reproduce.

5

"THE PARK

ON THE SOUND"

The lighted destination signs on the northbound cars of the Lexington Avenue subway read PELHAM BAY PARK. Where the subway tunnels out of the earth and becomes elevated along Westchester Avenue in the Bronx, riders blink at the sunlight and stare at a gray grid of six-story tenements and smoking factories. Passing through Mott Haven and Hunt's Point into the Soundview–Clason's Point section the scenery begins to shift from the grim building formulas of yesterday to the sterile ones of today. This is project land: here, in public housing and publicity aided middle-income housing projects, 8,325 apartments constructed since 1960 are home to nearly thirty thousand people. Tall ceramic brick towers sprout out of fields of wildflowers as new projects are added each year to the reclaimed East Bronx marshes. Then the building density begins to thin out and modest two-story attached houses appear. Finally, at the Bruckner Expressway the subway terminates and the green two-thousand-acre expanse of Pelham Bay Park begins.

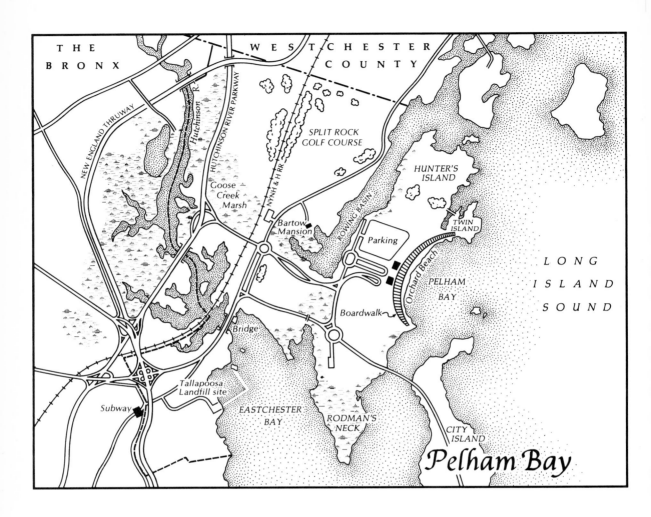

THE BRONX

WESTCHESTER COUNTY

NEW ENGLAND THRUWAY

Hutchinson R.

HUTCHINSON RIVER PARKWAY

NYNH & H RR

Goose Creek Marsh

SPLIT ROCK GOLF COURSE

ROWING BASIN

HUNTER'S ISLAND

TWIN ISLAND

Bartow Mansion

Parking

Orchard Beach

PELHAM BAY

LONG ISLAND SOUND

Boardwalk

Bridge

Subway

Tallapoosa Landfill site

EASTCHESTER BAY

RODMAN'S NECK

CITY ISLAND

Pelham Bay

The nineteenth-century men who fought to preserve this land from subsequent tides of urbanization were at least as prescient as those who fought to create Central Park. A citizens' group calling itself the Park Association was formed in 1881 for the purpose of urging the acquisition of "parks beyond the Harlem," in what was then Westchester County.

The recommendations of the group's report were embodied in a bill which was passed by the state legislature authorizing the purchase of land for Van Cortlandt, Bronx, Pelham Bay, Crotona and Claremont parks and their related parkways. After a lengthy battle led by Mayor Grace, who challenged the constitutionality of the bill and declared the whole parks scheme a "swindle," the bill was upheld by the courts and the land was purchased.

Pelham Bay, "the park on the Sound," was considered to be one of the choicest emeralds in the new civic crown. It was extolled by one of the authors of the report:

> *As a seaside park, and within easy reach by rail and boat of our east side population, its popularity will increase year by year. . . . and what place so admirably adapted for the many excursions which are organized by benevolent societies and individuals every summer, and through which tens of thousands who could never otherwise hope to spend a day in the country are enabled to enjoy that pleasure and breathe the pure air of heaven? . . . Space, beauty and variety! Closed in on three sides by "water walls," roofed by "the brave o'erhanging firmament," how could such a spot fail to bring health to the body and peace to the mind?*

Even if described somewhat rhetorically, the virtues were real and are still being appreciated in the twentieth century by a group of park regulars who daily ride the Lexington Avenue subway to Pelham Bay. They are retired men for the most part, inconspicuous in their faded knit shirts and khakis, carrying worn canvas Gladstone bags in which they have packed lunches and outing paraphernalia. In the age of the astronaut when man is making lonely voyages into space to plant his footprint on the moon, these men come to the park to find companionship and to reaffirm their bond with the living earth.

As the Manhattan work force crams itself into the southbound morning trains, the regulars riding the almost empty northbound cars arrive at the end of the line and begin their half-mile walk to the park. The road from the subway leads over the Hutchinson River bridge, and in the summer-time it is lined with goldenrod and foxglove and Queen Anne's lace. The scenery is not entirely that of a country lane, however; and to study the landscape from the bridge is to recognize the behemoth urban machine of which Pelham Bay is a part.

As one looks east, the north bank of the river appears much the same as it must have appeared to Anne Hutchinson, a refugee from religious intol-erance in Puritan Massachusetts, when she stepped ashore with her little band of followers in 1642. Here the rocky shore strewn with seaweed and mussels is representative of the coastal beauty to be found throughout parts of New England. However, on the south bank the landscape has been thoroughly obliterated by garbage dumping. This side of the river is known as Tallapoosa landfill site — a seventy-five-acre mountain of refuse across which a procession of white Department of Sanitation trucks rumbles in a continuous file.

The story of the destruction of the five-thousand-acre salt marsh that once covered the East Bronx with a teeming wealth of marine and bird life can also be read on the opposite side of the Hutchinson River bridge looking west. Here Anne Hutchinson is reputed to have staked out her homesite, and here she and her followers met their tragic end. Her settle-ment was unhappily timed, for in 1642 the Siwanoy Indians who inhabited Pelham Bay, as well as the other Indians living around New Amsterdam, were in a vengeful mood because of the repressive policies of the Dutch governor Kieft. The Siwanoy made repeated suggestions that the settlers leave. When after several months they had not left, a raid was staged and everyone in the Hutchinson group was massacred, with the exception of one Hutchinson daughter, who was held captive until ransomed four years later.

Today on the spot where Mistress Hutchinson's cottage probably stood, the towers of Co-op City have added a new profile to the Bronx skyline. Co-op City, with a planned population of fifty to sixty thousand, is the

Co-op City, the Bronx.

largest housing project ever built in New York or any other American city. In order to undertake its construction the spongy marshland had to be stabilized with sandy sludge piped from Eastchester Bay, and now, where once redwing blackbirds nested in bayberry bushes, twenty-story apartment towers rise in bleak anonymity out of a barren, featureless plain.

The great East Bronx marsh has not been entirely erased by garbage and an expanding urban population, however, for just north of the Hutchinson River within Pelham Bay Park there are a fifty-acre remnant surrounding Goose Creek and another, smaller remnant flanking Bartow Creek. In these marshlands tall salt meadow cordgrass grows in the soggy

areas — along the marsh streams that feed the creeks and along the mosquito ditch embankments. On drier ground the short salt meadow cordgrass takes over, while further upland black grass, or juncus, which is actually not a grass but a member of the lily family, appears as a deeply contrasting dark green.

These different zones of vegetation reflect different plant tolerances for the salt water that periodically bathes the marsh. The shallow depressed areas of the marsh, called pannes, receive the heaviest concentration of salts, and in them, protruding from a blue-green algal mat, are the fleshy segmented glasswort plants. In late summer small feathery sea lavender blooms add an exquisite note to the marsh landscape.

Bartow Creek is a favorite haunt of such Pelham Bay regulars as Bill Seely, who journeys there every day on the subway from his two-room apartment on East Eighty-second Street in Manhattan. Like most of the other park regulars, Bill is retired. Five years ago he completed the last day of his twenty-five years with the city Department of Water Supply, Gas and Electricity. Since then, his pension and the natural bounty of the park have taken care of his modest needs. His skin has become a warm chestnut color from daily exposure to the sun, and his gap-toothed smile bespeaks an amiable personality. Talking about his life in the park, Bill says, "This park is the last of the Mohicans. It used to be you could find places like this all over for fishing and swimming and just enjoying nature, but no more."

The day for Bill is consumed in talking with friends, playing pinochle, and observing the wildlife of the park. Living in daily contact with nature, he loves to read the small signs which indicate the passage of animals through the marsh; blades of grass in a stream making a crudely constructed muskrat dam, a red fox's hole half concealed under vines of Virginia creeper, raccoon footprints beside the tidal inlet. He can watch with unending fascination a mother black duck teaching her ducklings to swim in the protected waters of Bartow Creek, or at low tide a spotted sandpiper searching along its muddy banks for food.

There is something shy and sandpiperlike about the Bartow Creek regulars like Bill. Coming across the Hutchinson River bridge from the subway, they will veer suddenly into the undergrowth and disappear from sight. Inconspicuous footpaths trail through jewelweed and goldenrod or

67

Bartow Creek salt marsh, Pelham Bay Park.

meander into the tall mat of phragmites reeds bordering the marsh. Trunk paths lead to established meeting places: a flat-topped rock, a ring of stones, a rudely constructed picnic table. Branch paths go to individual hideouts where in careful concealment park regulars have stashed away private property: a fishing rod, an extra pair of shoes, a teapot or bottle of brandy.

Sometimes a hideout can serve a deeply personal purpose. One regular — a woman — has like Anne Hutchinson found Pelham Bay a refuge for her religious practice and worships at a little shrine which she has made by hanging a cardboard representation of the Virgin on an oak tree. Nearby beneath a white-painted cross a flame-blackened boulder is covered with wax drippings from the innumerable candles she has lit.

The humid, still air over Bartow Creek marsh is broken only by the chirruping of cicadas and the occasional whine of a jet engine overhead. This was not the case on October 18, 1776, when the marsh resounded with rifle fire as four thousand British soldiers under the command of General Howe landed on the Hutchinson River shore and began their advance toward White Plains. American patriots numbering fewer than eight hundred lay in ambush. Under the command of Colonel Glover fifty men fired into the British ranks and temporarily arrested their progress. The patriots then fell back behind a stone wall where they were joined by other recruits under Colonel Read. When the army was thirty yards away they fired point-blank, causing the enemy to scatter. The British summoned reinforcements, and an incessant rain of gunfire continued as the Americans fell back behind a second stone wall where Colonel Shepherd lay in wait with his men. There were seventeen volleys in all before Colonel Shepherd gave the command for his troops to retire to a third line of defense. When the skirmish was over only twelve Americans were dead; the British loss was estimated at a thousand.

At the time of the Revolution the lands encompassed by Pelham Bay Park were still in the hands of the Pell family, which owned three thousand acres of the original tract of 9,160 acres which Thomas Pell had purchased from the Indians in 1654, the remainder having been sold to one Jacob Leisler for a Huguenot settlement. Close by the path which Bill Seely takes to his Bartow Creek hideout are two trees, an elm and a mulberry, enclosed by an iron fence. They commemorate another tree, known

Freshwater stream feeding
Bartow Creek salt marsh, Pelham Bay Park.

as Treaty Oak, marking the spot where Thomas Pell conducted his transaction with the Siwanoy. Records show that his purchase was at least as shrewd as Peter Minuit's famous Manhattan bargain.

Thomas Pell's nephew and successor, John Pell, built a manor house in 1675 near the site of the present Bartow Mansion, and it was occupied by his descendents until the Revolution, when as loyalists they were forced to flee. After the war John Bartow, who married a Pell daughter, bought 220 acres, which included the manor parcel. Various portions of the original Pell tract were sold off over the years, including the manor parcel, which John Bartow disposed of in 1813. The manor property returned to the family, however, when Robert Bartow, John Bartow's grandson, repurchased it in 1836 and built on it his splendid Greek Revival mansion. The Bartow Mansion, which was included in the 1888 transaction which reassembled various portions of the old Pell estate into Pelham Bay Park, was allowed to deteriorate over the years until in 1914 it was leased by the city of New York to the International Garden Club. That organization undertook its restoration and the construction of a large sunken garden in the rear. It exists now in melancholy grandeur, infrequently visited, its genteel quiet unbroken by the sounds of domestic life.

In Pelham Bay Park the practice of horticulture is not confined to the mansion grounds. For the Bartow Creek regulars like Bill Seely, who live in city apartments, growing things in the earth fills a basic and important need. Hidden in the phragmites reeds and in the secluded upland bordering the marsh are patches of cleared land — little flowerbeds and "victory" gardens lovingly tended by Bill and his friends.

In addition to gardening, the Bartow Creek regulars spend a good deal of time fishing in the protected waters of the tidal inlet. Their catches include flounder, eel, tomcod and occasionally a striped bass. The inlet was also a popular fishing ground with the Indians three hundred years ago. Masses of oyster shells, wood ashes and other fragments were discovered by park archaeologists indicating that the shore in front of the Bartow Mansion was an important fishing camp. The Indian shell heaps and other archaeological evidence were destroyed when dredged materials were heaped upon them during the construction of the Olympic rowing basin in the 1950's.

The rowing basin itself is the by-product of an even greater landscape

A shrine by the shore, Pelham Bay Park.

Twin Island regulars, Pelham Bay Park.

alteration: the construction of Orchard Beach by Robert Moses in the 1930's. Originally, Hunter's Island and Rodman's Neck were discrete landmasses, and the waters of Long Island Sound washed in between them. Then millions of cubic yards of garbage mixed with sandy fill were deposited, connecting the two. White sand was spread in a curving arc two hundred feet wide and a mile long over the garbage fill, creating the beach and its adjacent parking lot. This consolidation enclosed the waters in front of the Bartow Mansion in a long fingerlike lagoon which was later carved into the rowing basin.

Like the gulls who in winter congregate in the Orchard Beach parking lot and along the shore, the men who meet on Hunter's Island are a more gregarious breed than the men like Bill Seely who frequent the marsh. Within each group there is a strict sense of territoriality which extends to subgroups or colonies, little bands ranging from a lone individual to perhaps as many as twenty who have staked a claim to a particular piece of land — a rock outcropping, a grove of trees, a section of shoreline. Colonies are organized primarily along ethnic lines.

Although the Russians on Hunter's Island form the largest colony, the Germans are probably the largest group among park regulars. They are subdivided into several colonies. There is a great deal of bantering among immigrants from different German principalities, even though they may be members of the same colony. After someone has lost at chess or pinochle, his opponent will say, "Well, there now — what can you expect from a Westphalian!"

"Ha!" the loser will retort. "You Bavarians, always trying to win by cheating!"

This friendly Teutonic rivalry has been going on in Pelham Bay Park for the past twenty years. One of the regulars claims to have instigated the whole movement back in the 1920's when he invited a friend from a German society in Yorkville to come up to the park with him. Soon all the members of the society were meeting in the park, as many as a hundred or more.

In the memory of all the regulars those were grand times indeed. Wives and sweethearts came, and children, and there were frequent parties and always coffee klatches. At that time the northern tip of Twin Island was the focal point of their activity, and it soon became rimmed with little encampments — rude shelters fashioned of stones carried from the shore. Railroad ties and planks were used to make benches and tables; pieces of plywood were positioned so they could be put over the shelters in case of rain. There were fireplaces for cooking and for warmth in winter; utensils and dishes were cunningly concealed when not in use. But the Park Department took exception to this unauthorized domesticity and Moses had the encampments razed. After this some of the regulars went to Hunter's Island and built new camps; others stayed and reconstructed their places on Twin Island. Such is the sense of territoriality among some regulars that they have rebuilt their shelters time and time again in the same spot after vandalism or some other catastrophe has destroyed them.

Back in the 1920's when Hunter's Island was still an island, the regulars would walk north from the subway to an old wooden bridge which connected the Hunter estate with the mainland. Crossing the bridge, they would walk up the drive that had once clattered with carriage wheels as visitors rode through the massive gateway to the stately mansion on the top of the hill.

John Hunter, who bought the island in the early nineteenth century, had been keenly interested in politics and had entertained lavishly. One famous guest was President Martin Van Buren, who stayed with Hunter in 1839. The *Herald Tribune* recorded not only the visit but the contents of the house as well. According to the report, the President sat on Chippendale dining room chairs and was surrounded by paintings by the most eminent old masters: Titian, Rubens, Rembrandt and Leonardo.

The house itself was built in 1812 in the Georgian style. According to one historian, "It was square two-story and basement . . . with one-story balanced wings . . . quoined stone corners . . . stone windows. In the façades were Palladian windows. Across the rear was a comfortable verandah overlooking the formal terraced gardens, reaching down to the water's edge. The style of the mansion was so similar to the style of the old City Hall of New York City, that the two structures might well have been the work of the same architect."

After the acquisition of Pelham Bay Park by the city, Hunter's Mansion sat vacant and derelict, a target of vandals. At the time of the Orchard Beach construction Robert Moses ordered it demolished. Today its remains can be traced in the half-buried rubble of the old stable and in the red sandstone supports for the gateposts, which are embedded in the earth on either side of the barely discernible drive leading up from the now vanished bridge. Red sandstone column bases from the portico can be found mixed with native rocks in the little causeway connecting Hunter's and Twin islands that was built at the time the mansion was destroyed.

At the crest of the hill where the mansion once stood is a small brick concession house built by Moses. The concession was operated for one year, but business was slight and it was closed and has remained closed ever since. The paved asphalt apron in front of the unused concession house is the meeting place for Otto Kramer and his friends. Originally the group had a homemade retreat near the shore, but one year the mosqui-

75

A Hunter's Island regular.

Great horned owl wintering in Pelham Bay Park.

toes were particularly troublesome, and in an effort to avoid them Otto and his friends moved to the abandoned terrace.

The deep, shady woods around the concession house are cool in contrast to the humid marsh. So wild and beautiful is the Hunter's Island forest that it is easy to imagine the awed wonder with which Thomas Pell and those other early settlers beheld a virgin continent. Though the original plant life has been considerably altered by imported species, the sensuous mystery of the forest still prevails. Blue jays shriek in the green upper stories of oak and hickory. In summer beneath a grove of black locusts young robins, the year's second brood, show their spotted breasts, while noisy starlings compete for the ripe burgundy pellets hanging from the black cherry trees. Jewelweed grows waist high with bright orange-spotted gold pendants glowing against the dark green leaves.

Otto Kramer is a retired tool and die worker who lives in nearby Mount Vernon. Every day after tending to his rose garden in the morning he walks over to the park to spend an amiable day playing cards and chess

The southernmost extension of the rocky New England coastline, Pelham Bay Park.

with his friends on the concession-house terrace. Otto came to America in 1927 from the East German province of Saxony. His friend William Schmidt, who is a Bavarian, likes to make much of this fact. "Don't you think Otto looks like a Russian?" he will inquire. "You can tell he doesn't have the real German look," says the apple-cheeked Schmidt. When checkmated by Otto in a game of chess, he will declare, "Well, now, there's a Saxon for you!"

Often when the weather is warm the regulars will go for a swim. Shunning the crowded sands of Orchard Beach, they prefer to bathe off the rocky shore. Here on Hunter's Island is the most southerly segment of the geologically young New England coastline, whose bedrock was scoured by glaciation seventeen thousand years ago. As the ice melted, the rising waters covered the sandy sediments of the coastal plain and filled the coastal valleys, creating a "drowned" shoreline. Here and there bedrock outcroppings formed small offshore islands, several of which dot the waters of Pelham Bay.

The boulders balanced along the Hunter's Island shore are additional reminders of the Ice Age. These huge rocks were plucked from bedrock in Westchester and Connecticut and shoved southward by the ice mass to be left during the glacial retreat. Two Hunter's Island erratics were of special significance to the Indians, who named them Mishow and Gray Mare.

The story of the coastal geology of Pelham Bay is by no means complete, and, as has already been remarked, geologists are still studying it. Previous theory held that its outcrops of gray-banded gneiss and mica-flecked schist were part of the same rock formation that underlies Manhattan Island and the western part of the Bronx; but now this assumption has been invalidated, and the Pelham Bay rocks have been tentatively assigned to the Westchester coastal sequence and provisionally labeled the Hutchinson River group.

The rocky Pelham Bay shore is zoned at different levels into distinct bands of sea life, which becomes increasingly visible as the tide goes out. Clinging to the seaward sides of rocks are barnacles, and below the barnacles are masses of rockweed (*Fucus adentatus*), rubbery brown algae with small yellowish bladders, common to rocky coasts. Mixed with the *Fucus* are the gleaming wet sheets of green sea lettuce (*Ulva*). Blue mussels (*Mysticus edulis*) appear in this zone. In the third zone, below the band

Glacial erratic revered by the Indians, Pelham Bay Park.

of barnacles and the zone of rockweed, is red algae, otherwise known as Irish moss (*Chondrus crispus*). Mussels are present here also, and at low tide the regulars wade into the shallow water to pick them off the sea floor. Large clams are also gathered for making clam chowder.

Food from the land as well as from the sea is collected in the Park. In late May wild strawberries form an inconspicuous mat close to the ground in the woods of Hunter's Island, and they are quickly picked by the regulars. The thorny blackberry bushes, which in the spring bear white flowers on the tangled brambles of previous years' growth while new un-flowered spires grow erect beside them, by August have borne fruit. The Russian regulars, whose encampment is at the northern tip of Hunter's Island on a small promontory, use the berries to make blackberry wine. Actually, the beverage they concoct is somewhat stronger than wine. First the blackberries which they collect are allowed to ferment for a couple of weeks with sugar; then the decanted syrup is combined with pure alcohol in proportions of one to one. These spirits are stored until Christmastime, when an annual celebration is held.

The Russians have a communal dinghy in which they row out to collect pieces of driftwood which they burn for logs in the wintertime. They also manage to catch a good many fish from their boat. Sometimes they will sell the fish to the other regulars, a three-pound bluefish bringing a dollar.

After summer showers, mushrooms spring up in the moist grasses of Hunter's Island. They are gathered by several of the park regulars, whose practiced eyes can discriminate between the safe and the poisonous species. Otto often brings them home, and slices them together with onions, and fries them in butter. With boiled potatoes, he says, you could not have a finer meal.

Besides mushrooms, there are pheasants in the grasses around the concession-house terrace. If startled, a nesting female will rise up with a great whirring of wings and fly away while her small young scurry for safety. Otto has seen raccoons in the park and once three years ago he saw a white-tailed deer. "But the kids, they come with bows and arrows or BB guns," he says sadly.

There is no game warden patrolling Pelham Bay Park, and in addition to animal slaughter by juveniles, there is a good deal of adult poaching.

Although they are almost never molested by the regulars, rabbits, squirrels, and ducks are often killed for food by other park visitors.

In the recollection of the regulars the birds of the park are not as numerous as they were in the past. "There used to be all kinds of birds, you wouldn't believe how many," says Otto's friend William Schmidt. "But, you know, they started the mosquito spraying and a lot of the birds disappeared."

On the other side of the ledger, additional birds have been attracted to the park because of the assistance of the regulars who put seed-packed chunks of suet in the trees in winter. In 1958, naturalist John Kieran noted that the redheaded woodpecker was no longer found in the New York City range, but ten years later, through the efforts of some of the regulars, this bird was persuaded to spend the winter in Pelham Bay Park.

Although the groups that meet today are primarily stag, some wives accompany their husbands, particularly on weekends, and a few widows continue coming to the park. Gone, however, are the children, for the next generation will have none of the old-country airs indulged in by their parents. As one regular explains, "All the kids have cars. Now they won't come anymore." Most of the children have families of their own and have moved to the suburbs. Otto Kramer's daughter lives in Yorkville Heights with her husband and two children. On weekends Otto visits them. He spends his time cultivating their garden while his son-in-law mows the grass with his new power mower. Otto complains because the daughter's husband, even though he comes from a Ukrainian farming family in Pennsylvania, feels that gardening is undignified.

Even the old-timers are disappearing from the park as one by one they die off. One of the Bartow Creek regulars who commutes by subway to the park from Woodside, Long Island, says in describing his passion for the park, "Coming from the old country we have the love of nature. For me sitting here looking at the water, that's my tranquilizer. I don't need anything else." He would like to move to Co-op City and has investigated the possibility of buying an apartment there. "But I'm seventy years old, and they're still not finished building. We're all dying," he says matter-of-factly.

6

"DAYS AFIELD

ON STATEN ISLAND"

This appearance of the bold lacing-together, across the
waters, of the scattered members of the monstrous organism
— lacing as by the ceaseless play of an enormous system of
steam-shuttles or electric bobbins (I scarce know what to call
them), commensurate in form with their infinite work — does
perhaps more than anything else to give the pitch of the
vision of energy. One has the sense that the monster grows
and grows, flinging abroad its loose limbs even as some
unmannered young giant at his "larks," and that the binding
stitches must for ever fly further and faster and draw harder;
the future complexity of the web, all under the sky and over
the sea, becoming thus that of some colossal set of clockworks,
some steel-souled machine-room of brandishing arms and
hammering fists and opening and closing jaws. The
immeasurable bridges are but as the horizontal sheaths of
pistons working at high pressure, day and night, and subject,
one apprehends with perhaps inconsistent gloom, to certain, to
fantastic, to merciless multiplication. In the light of this
apprehension indeed the breezy brightness of the Bay puts on
the semblance of the vast white page that awaits beyond any
other perhaps the black overscoring of science.
                    Henry James, The American Scene

In 1524 a three-masted carrack, the *Dauphine*,
named in honor of the young dauphin of France, appeared in New York
Harbor. Its captain, Giovanni da Verrazano, described the Upper Bay as
a "very beautiful lake" and named it the Bay of St. Marguerite in honor
of Marguerite of Angoulême, sister of King Francis I, the patron of his
voyage. The seafaring party, welcomed by natives "uttering very great
exclamations of admiration," landed briefly on Staten Island, leaving
hastily at the onset of a storm "with much regret because of its conven-
ience and beauty, thinking it was not without some properties of value, all
of its hills showing indications of minerals."

Because of this tantalizing first glimpse through New York's constricted
harbor passageway, Verrazano's name is memorialized in the Verrazano-Narrows Bridge, the world's longest suspension bridge, which arcs
above it. The bridge, finished some four hundred forty years after the
Dauphine's historic visit, is the needle that stitches insular Staten Island

The Verrazano Bridge, "the needle that stitches insular Staten Island to the surrounding urban fabric."

to the surrounding urban fabric. The island is no longer isolated and remote; its home construction rate has doubled in the years since the bridge began to decant the Brooklyn bourgeoisie into status-styled, look-alike developer's houses that each year push farther south along Hylan Boulevard.

Post-bridge growth has sent the highway engineers to their drawing boards; their plans include a six-lane "drive" rimming the south shore and the controversial Richmond Parkway running down the central spine of the island. But mixed with the chaos of hasty urbanization have been some successful attempts to save the old island with its forested hilltops and quiet glacial ponds from the onslaught of the bulldozer. The most notable victory for conservationists to date has been the redesignation of

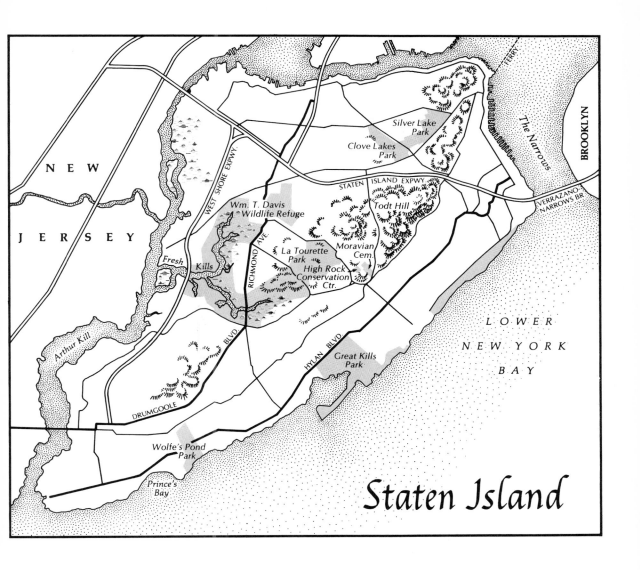

N E W
J E R S E Y

Fresh
Kills

Arthur Kill

WEST SHORE EXPWY.

RICHMOND AVE.

BLVD.

DRUMGOOLE

HYLAN BLVD.

Wm. T. Davis
Wildlife Refuge

La Tourette
Park

High Rock
Conservation
Ctr.

Moravian
Cem.

Todt Hill

STATEN ISLAND EXPWY.

Clove Lakes
Park

Silver Lake
Park

FERRY

The Narrows

BROOKLYN

VERRAZANO-
NARROWS BR.

LOWER
NEW YORK
BAY

Great Kills
Park

Wolfe's Pond
Park

Prince's
Bay

Staten Island

Glacial pond, Todt Hill, Staten Island, circa 1906.

the Richmond Parkway route, saving the land originally acquired for the highway as a woodland corridor — a representative remnant of Staten Island's pre-urban ecology.

This corridor today forms a chain of open spaces including Todt Hill — the highest point on the eastern seaboard south of Blue Hill, Massachusetts — the historic Moravian Cemetery, High Rock Conservation center, and LaTourette Park, and is the eastern arm of a U-shaped greenbelt. The western arm contains the William T. Davis Wildlife Refuge, a combination of marsh and woodland. Within this green U flow the branching tributaries of Fresh Kills, the drainage system for the once vast marshes that covered the western end of the island. Today much of this marshland has been obliterated by the marine landfill operations of the Department of Sanitation; ten thousand tons of New York refuse are barged to Fresh Kills every day.

To visit the greenbelt at High Rock Conservation Center or the Davis Refuge on an early spring day is to step backward in time and to forget

86

about garbage and highways and the raw scraped land of the new housing developments. Catkin tassels sway below the still partially curled, soft new leaves of the oak trees. The maples hold their flowers erect; their winged samaras float beneath. The forest floor is carpeted with trout lily and Canada mayflower. There are false Solomon's seal and false lily of the valley, their tiny blossoms as yet unfurled. In the low swampy places grow the scarlet-flowered red maples and skunk cabbages with their large, sour-smelling leaves. The flower part of the skunk cabbage, the spathe, a curious, mottled "hood" that shoulders its way through the frosty ground of late winter, has long since disappeared. The yellow blossoms of another early bloomer, the spicebush, have begun to fade as new leaves are put forth. Within a grove of sweetgum trees the ground is littered with last year's spiny, hollow seedpods, while above their rough trunks smooth, silvery branches are covered with galaxies of newly formed, star-shaped leaves.

Besides the forest-covered hills and marsh fringes of the greenbelt, there are Staten Island's surf-beat beaches and bays and creeks. Perhaps because of its beautiful and richly varied natural endowment, Staten Island has been an especially productive breeding ground and laboratory for young naturalists. In the nineteenth century, when the natural science professions were mostly in their infancy, the island produced an abundant crop of careers. Of the older generation, those active in the late part of the century, were the geologists Louis Pope Gratacap and John J. Crooke, and the botanists Nathaniel L. Britton and Arthur Hollick. Britton and Hollick were the co-authors of a definitive volume, *Flora of Richmond County*, which remains the definitive study of the botany of the island.

A younger generation, which made its contribution to unraveling the mysteries of natural science on Staten Island and also achieved professional distinction in the world at large, was made up of a trio of high school friends: James Chapin, who became an ornithologist with the American Museum of Natural History and a member of the expedition that assembled the museum's first collection of the birds of Africa; Alonson Skinner, whose discoveries of Indian remains on Staten Island led him to become an archaeologist; and Howard Cleaves, a pioneer wildlife photographer and lecturer on the Audubon circuit. Cleaves, now an octogenarian and the last survivor of his generation of island-bred professional naturalists, still pursues ornithology with the undiminished enthusiasm of his boyhood and has the distinction of being the founder of the only colony of purple martins within the boundaries of New York City.

Cleaves installed his first martin house, an eleven-dollar, twelve-apartment Sears, Roebuck model, on the banks of Lemon Creek beside Prince's Bay in 1951. That year two pairs of martins nested, depositing four eggs in each nest. One pair abandoned their nest of eggs; three eggs in the other nest hatched, but the young birds were killed when still in the pinfeather stage by the driving rain of a hard northeasterly storm. The following year brought more disappointment; not a single pair nested.

But in 1953 the martin house lodged six breeding pairs; and a decade later, in 1963, with accommodations enlarged to seven houses, seventy-five breeding pairs took advantage of Cleaves's hospitality. In recent years this figure has declined somewhat. Cleaves speculates that in Brazil, where the birds winter, young boys kill them for food. Occasionally, too, the advance guard will arrive back on Staten Island in early April when it may be too cold, and some have died that way.

By the third week in May, breeding mates have selected their cubicles and have begun nest building. In mid-July, when the young birds are well feathered, they are taught to fly; a month later they are ready to accompany their parents on the long migration to South America.

Like an airport tower operator Cleaves carefully monitors all the departing flights. I asked him to keep me posted on the birds' leavetaking, and on August 20, 1969, I received the following letter:

> *I have been checking to determine the final departure date for 1969. One individual youngster of the 1969 issue persists in roosting nightly; all the rest are gone. The bulk of the colony left between two and three weeks ago. Then for several nights three individuals roosted, and now there is but the one left. The last three nights I was free to make a check — August 16th, 17th and 19th — the bird roosted in one of the rooms on the north side of House #5, and these are the rooms in which no martins nested this season.*

This one lingering martin remains quite silent, arriving from his day afield shortly before eight o'clock, resting for some minutes on a high wire, then proceeding to the porch of the martin house. After spending a few minutes there, he enters a room, then looks out the door for another few minutes before disappearing into the chamber for the night, at about five to ten minutes past eight o'clock. He must be lonesome, but loath to leave the conventional sleeping quarters. After the birds leave they sleep in leafy trees at night. In Baton Rouge, La., they roost on the girders of an oil refinery. I think I showed you a flashlight of that situation.

Sincerely,
Howard H. Cleaves

Cleaves's hospitality is not confined to the martins. He has put up tree swallow nest boxes in the Moravian Cemetery and at the South Shore Country Club. Vandalism of the nesting boxes has remained a problem; for that reason his most successful tree swallow operation is conducted at the fenced-in Oakwood Beach sewage treatment plant at the northern edge of Great Kills Park. Great Kills, once a vast salt marsh bordered by bayberries and beach plums, was used as a garbage dump in the 1920's. The park today is for the most part a waving sea of phragmites reeds; the grounds of the sewage treatment plant have been landscaped with London plane trees, and the grass is a lush carpet of green fertilized by the organically rich sludge derived as a by-product of the treatment process. On the trunks of the plane trees Cleaves has fastened his tree swallow boxes. A remnant of bayberry bushes still grows at Great Kills, providing the tiny aromatic waxy berries much loved by these birds.

The men who run the sewage treatment plant are enthusiastic bird watchers. Besides allowing Cleaves to put up his tree swallow boxes they permit barn swallows to inhabit the plant. The birds use mud to fasten their nests to the large pipes that circle one huge room a few inches below the ceiling. It is an extraordinary sight to see the parent swallows darting in and out of the cavernous chamber gathering insects to feed their voracious young, who wait with mouths agape, indifferent to the strong smell of sodium hydrochloride that fills the air.

James Paul Chapin holds a baby barred owl, Staten Island, 1909.

Alonson Skinner (left) stands with William Thompson Davis (right) on the sands at Crooke's Point (Great Kills), Staten Island, 1909.

Boys today on Staten Island.

Less common than the barn or tree swallow is the rough-winged swallow, who likes to make its home near water. Cleaves told me that for several years a small colony of these birds has nested in the girders supporting the concrete bridge where Hylan Boulevard crosses Lemon Creek.

But changes are coming fast to Staten Island as its post–Verrazano Bridge development accelerates. The Planning Commission's proposed upgrading and widening of Hylan Boulevard may accommodate progress, but it will not help the rough-winged swallows. The shore drive which is proposed would obliterate the bank of Lemon Creek where the purple martin houses now stand. A war memorial stadium is planned for Great Kills Park; its parking lot may decimate the remaining bayberry bushes with their fruit prized by Cleaves's tree swallows. The fields and vacant lots with their nourishing supply of insects are fast being blanketed by "model" homes, and this will surely affect the barn swallows.

Whenever he thinks of these things Cleaves is glad that most of his life on Staten Island has been spent in its semirural days before the bridge. "Now Staten Island is ruined," he says matter-of-factly.

Bridging Cleaves's generation with that of the early, nineteenth-century naturalists was William T. Davis, the founder of the refuge that bears his name. A versatile naturalist whose specialty was entomology, he made a lifelong study of cicadas, particularly the seventeen-year locust. As a youth he was a disciple of the entomologist Augustus Grote and went on field expeditions with Hollick, Britton and Gratacap. Later, in turn, he became the mentor of Chapin, Skinner and Cleaves and would accompany the boys on long rambles all over the island. Cleaves recalls how Davis was capturing insects with his net and vials, while he and Chapin were scrambling up trees to examine owls' nests, and Skinner, his eyes glued to the ground, was on the scout for Indian artifacts. The essence of rambles such as these is vividly captured in a slender little volume called *Days Afield on Staten Island* which Davis published at his own expense in 1892 and which has since become a kind of minor classic in the literature of nature. At that time Davis could admire across the island's entire breadth such wild unaltered nature as is today confined to the greenbelt: "The red maples are aglow, the pussy willows invite the bees and those big burly flies, with hairy bodies, that fly with ponderous inaccuracy. The marsh marigolds spread their yellow flowers, and the hermit thrush sits silently on the trees, his shadow cast, mayhap, in some dark, leaf-laden pool."

Another shadow was even then beginning to creep across Staten Island, for as Davis lamented in his journal: "Houses appear where it used to be uninhabited. I see the clothes drying on the line where once I saw wild ducks, so I have to abandon a little of my rambling ground every year." Davis, of course, was witnessing the first phase of Staten Island's now accelerated suburbanization. Before that, however, the landscape of the island had undergone several other transformations.

Its hilly central spine of serpentine, a greenish rock, is composed of ferromagnesian minerals. Crustal uplift and erosion caused the serpentine to be exposed at surface level during Pleistocene time; glaciation plucked away large chunks of it, revealing pockets of iron. In writing of Staten Island in 1670, Daniel Denton remarked that "tin and store of iron ore and calamine store is said likewise to be found there." The Dutch name for Todt Hill was Yserberg (Iron Hill), and iron was in fact mined there. A hundred years ago the fibrous serpentine was also mined near Tompkinsville and used for the same purpose as asbestos.

Several geologic eons after the formation of the serpentine, another igneous rock, the Palisades diabase, was formed. Rising as ramparts along the New Jersey shore of the Hudson River, this sloping rock formation penetrates Staten Island, sinking belowground a few hundred yards west of the Davis Refuge in the community of Travis. Cradled between the serpentine and the diabase is a bed of glacial outwash, whose water-retentive gravel forms an aquafer. Here, cold, pure water used to burst spontaneously from the ground in such abundance as to suggest a name for the locality — Springville. The Springville aquafer was of commercial importance in the days before Catskill water was piped to Staten Island; in fact, the Davis Refuge owes its existence to the dissolution of the Crystal Water Company and the sale of its lands to the New York City Department of Parks. Water still percolates to the surface around the now capped wells, making boggy rings within the refuge forest.

The glacier that covered the northern four-fifths of Staten Island, eroding the iron-rich serpentine and depositing the gravel bed of the aquafer, retreated approximately seventeen thousand years ago. Seventy thousand years before that, Staten Island was a warm, semitropical swamp. Writing in 1909, the geologist Gratacap reconstructed the landscape of that remote time, the Cretaceous period of geologic history, as "a deeply foliaged low, outstretched forested plain, with sluggish streams, embayments, fresh lagoons, and swampy ponds, on which a sun of semi-tropical intensity shone with changing accidents of storm and flood and steaming fog, while a persistent sedimentation in the whirling or quiescent waters built up the clay reefs, shoals, and beds." These deposits, termed the Magothy formation by later geologists, can be seen around Tottenville and Kreischerville at the unglaciated southern tip of the island. The clay beds at Kreischerville were used during the second half of the nineteenth century for the manufacture of fire bricks, drainpipes, gas retorts and other refractory ware. Because of the similarity of soil conditions, this part of the island supports the same botany as the New Jersey pine barrens.

By 1609, when Henry Hudson sailed the *Half Moon* into the waters so briefly visited by Verrazano eighty-five years before, Staten Island's postglacial vegetation had evolved into a thick forest "full of great and tall oaks," according to Robert Juet, the diarist of the voyage. Occupying the island were the Leni-Lenape Indians, whom Juet described as going "in deer skins loose, well-dressed." At the turn of this century, when William T. Davis used to spend days afield with his protégé Alonson Skinner, the Staten Island shore was dotted with shell heaps and mounds of Indian artifacts. Thoreau spent a year on the island in 1843, and after visiting a farm on the marshy shores of the Arthur Kill, he wrote home to his sister Helen in Concord: "As I was coming away I took my toll out of the soil in the shape of arrow-heads — which may after all be the surest crop — certainly not affected by drought."

The landscape of the island was altered little during its centuries of Indian occupation. When the Dutch ruled New Amsterdam, fitful attempts at colonization were begun, but they were doomed because of the repressive policies of Director Kieft. On January 5, 1639, the patroon David Piertsz DeVries, to whom title to the island had been granted, sent over a group of people to settle it. A few months later some of DeVries's swine were stolen by the New Jersey Raritans, and Kieft, against DeVries's wishes, sent one hundred troops from Fort Amsterdam to exact revenge. According to DeVries's description of the incident, several Indians were killed and the brother of the chief was captured and "misused

. . . in his private parts with a piece of wood." He adds that "such acts of tyranny were . . . far from making friends with the inhabitants." Another patroon, Cornelis Melyn, also attempted settlement, but his colony was twice wiped out, once during the Whiskey War of 1643, and again during the Peach War of 1655.

Under English rule after 1664, settlement of the island began in earnest. In 1670 a treaty was signed with the Indians whose absolute (and this time final) surrender of possession was symbolized by the presentation to Governor Lovelace of "a sod and a shrub or branch of every kind of tree which grows on the island, except the ash and elder." Included in this arboreal contribution no doubt was a representative of the sturdy chestnut, which along with the oaks remarked by Juet dominated the island's scenery until its decimation by the pernicious fungus blight that killed all American chestnut trees during the first part of this century. Before its demise, however, the chestnut played a leading role in the development of the island; according to one nineteenth-century historian it was "laid under heavy contribution" for such things as fence posts and rails, telegraph and telephone poles, and railroad ties.

When the Dutch preacher Danckaerts and his friend Sluyter spent three days touring Staten Island in 1679, there were living there about "a hundred families of which the English constitute the least portion, and the Dutch and French divide between them equally the greater portion." The travelers also observed: "Game of all kinds is plenty, and twenty-five and thirty deer are sometimes seen in a herd. . . . We tasted here the best grapes. . . . About one-third part of the distance from the south side to the west end is still all woods, and is very little visited. We had to go along the shore, finding sometimes fine creeks provided with wild turkeys, geese, snipes and wood hens. Lying rotting on the shore were thousands of fish called *marsbancken* [menhaden], which are about the size of common carp."

In 1748, when the naturalist Peter Kalm was commissioned by the great Swedish botanist Linnaeus to catalogue American native plant life, much of the forest which Danckaerts and Sluyter had traveled through had been cleared and a prosperous agricultural community established. Kalm wrote: "The prospect of the country here is extremely pleasing, as it is not so much intercepted by woods, but offers more cultivated fields to

"The broad rolling plain along the shore became a smiling pastoral landscape of fields and hedgerows." Staten Island landscape by Jasper Cropsey, circa 1852.

view." He noticed apple orchards everywhere and at each farmhouse a cider press; cherry trees grew near the gardens, and "all travellers are allowed to pluck ripe fruit in any garden they pass by; and not even the most covetous farmers can hinder them from so doing." One hundred years later Thoreau, too, remarked that "peaches, and especially cherries grow by all the fences."

Kalm's diary includes a description of the Fresh Kills marshes: "The country was low on both sides of the river, and consisted of meadows. But there was no other hay to be got, than such as commonly grows on swampy grounds; for as the tide comes up this river [Arthur Kill], these low plains were sometimes overflowed when the water was high."

Branching through the marsh were the twisting estuarine creeks and rivulets that fed Fresh Kills. In the days before the Fresh Kills marshes were smothered by garbage, both Richmond Creek and Main Creek were navigable for more than a mile. Boatmen gave the little capes along the route such names as Neverfail Point, Point No Point, and Cedar Bush Point. At the mouth of Fresh Kills was an island alternately, and ominously, named Deadman's Island and Burnt Island. Throughout the marsh were other "islands," which were not true islands but simply hummocks protruding out of the surrounding moist and tide-inundated land. Many, like Lake's Island, visited by Thoreau, were studded with Indian artifacts.

Thirty years after Kalm's visit Staten Island, like the surrounding mainland, was engulfed by the Revolution. It was in British occupation for the duration of the war; its hilltops were cleared and used for redoubts; its forests were all chopped down for firewood. There were still foxes and raccoons and opossums at this time; the last deer of the once large herds observed by Danckaerts and Sluyter was shot a few years after the war.

With the patriot victory, loyalist families from Staten Island fled to Nova Scotia. Farms that had been pillaged by the redcoats were returned to prosperity. A second-growth forest appeared upon the hillsides, and the broad, rolling plain along the shore became a smiling pastoral landscape of fields and hedgerows.

This was the Staten Island that charmed Thoreau as a young man when he became the tutor of Ralph Waldo Emerson's nephew Haven, son of William Emerson, a Staten Island judge. In a letter to his family soon after he arrived, he wrote, "The whole island is like a garden and affords very fine scenery."

In recommending Thoreau to his brother, the Concord Emerson had written, "I am sure no purer person lives in wide New York; and he is a bold and profound thinker though he may easily chance to pester you with some accidental crotchets and perhaps a village exaggeration of the value of facts." With his woodsman's morality, Thoreau scorned Wall Street and "Broadway with its wooden pavement." And if he exaggerated, it was not from overvaluing the facts but from being overpowered by first impressions. He wrote:

> I cannot realize that it is the roar of the sea I hear now, and not the wind in the Walden woods. . . . Everything here is on a grand and generous scale — sea-weed, water, and sand, and even the dead fishes, horses and hogs have a rank luxuriant odor. Great shad nets spread to dry, crabs and horse-shoes crawling over the sand — clumsy boats, only for service, dancing like sea-fowl on the surf, and ships afar off going about their

96

*business . . . I must live along the beach, on the southern
shore, which looks directly out to sea, and see what that great
parade of water means, that dashes and roars, and has not yet
wet me, as long as I have lived.*

Frederick Law Olmsted, a contemporary of Thoreau's and the landscape architect of Central Park, began his career as a farmer on Staten
Island. In 1848, five years after Thoreau had been exhilarated by his long
watery walks along the south shore, Olmsted acquired one hundred thirty
acres overlooking Prince's Bay. It was on this farm that Olmsted first
showed his genius for landscape construction. According to a friend, "he
moved the barns and all their belongings behind a knoll, he brought the
road in so that it approached the house by a graceful curve, he turfed the
borders of the pond and planted water plants on its edge and shielded it
from all contamination." Olmsted himself wrote: "I do exceedingly enjoy
the view from my house . . . bounded by the horizon — dark blue ocean,
with forever distant sails coming up or sinking as they bid good-bye to
America."

Olmsted's foray into the nursery business on Staten Island proved
financially unsuccessful, and the farm was sold in 1854. But his relationship with the island was renewed in 1870, when he was commissioned to
prepare the *Report to the Staten Island Improvement Commission of a
Preliminary Scheme of Improvements*.

During the intervening years the island had become notorious for its
malarial infestation. Shunning it, society located its suburban villas and
summer retreats in Westchester and on Long Island. Theodore Roosevelt's
father and grandfather had summered on a farm that is now part of the
William T. Davis Refuge; fearing for their health, the family ceased to go
there, and the farm was sold in 1878.

In 1748 Kalm had remarked of Staten Island: "The people hereabouts
are said to be troubled in summer with intense swarms of gnats or mosquitoes, which sting them and their cattle." In 1870 medical science had not
yet made the mosquito-malaria connection, and a great deal of Olmsted's
report, which he prepared in cooperation with a Dr. Elisha Harris, a
pioneer sanitarian, discusses prevailing medical opinion on the origins of
malaria. One theory held that the disease was caused by a "granular

microphyte: accompanied by a quantity of small spores, rainbow-tinted like spots of oil, growing on the surface of the marsh water." According to another, it was caused by "certain gases or volatile emanations . . . which are evolved by decaying vegetable matter under the required conditions of temperature and moisture." The latter hypothesis posed a more virulent threat since the vapors could be "wafted" and additional malaria bred wherever there were puddles of water upon which the sun shone.

Staten Island at that time had over one thousand pond holes whose stagnant waters the report characterized as "malarial nurseries." These small swamps were not entirely unprofitable; many were used for growing basket willows. However, Olmsted warned: "This condition of saturation of the soil locks up a treasure such as no other suburb, and probably no other community in North America, can possess; it poisons the air and threatens the ruin of the island by prejudicing the public against all parts of it as a residence." He proposed a system of thorough drainage by laying a network of open-jointed pipes three or four feet below the ground surface, graded so that the water would flow in descending channels to outfalls near the shore. In addition, he suggested that "free-spreading trees should be common" to provide the shade necessary to guard against "wafted malaria."

The Olmsted report also contained recommendations (none of which were ever acted upon) for laying out major roads and parks. And though malaria is no longer a scourge, Staten Island still suffers from poor drainage. Because an adequate system of sanitary sewers is lacking, residents are plagued by septic tanks backing up, a cause of more-contemporary health threats such as hepatitis.

Ten years after the Olmsted report, in 1880, Staten Island had a population of thirty-nine thousand living on farms and in villages scattered across the island; the desired suburban growth had not yet begun to take place at an appreciable rate. Grymes Hill was a fashionable enclave for old Staten Island families. At Pleasant Plains around Prince's Bay lived some three thousand oystermen and their families. On the opposite side of the island, in Mariner's Harbor beside Kill Van Kull, overlooking the green salt meadows of New Jersey, the pride of the newly rich oyster captains was displayed in fine mansions along elm-arched Richmond Terrace.

And perceptible to the eyes of a keen Staten Island watcher like Wil-

South Beach, Staten Island, circa 1900.

liam T. Davis, certain other changes were beginning to occur. In his diary and in *Days Afield* he observed alterations to the landscape he had known in his youth. Electric lights, first installed on Staten Island in 1885, shown bright at the amusement park in St. George. South Beach, which Danckaerts and Sluyter and later Thoreau had roamed, became in Davis's day a pleasure strip with galleries, dance halls and saloons. Davis remarked that "the unconscious sand is held at great price" and "waiters rush about with their trays, where once the crows devoured the lady crabs, and the crowd is as lithesome and gay as were the sand fleas of old."

On March 4, 1894, he wrote in his diary that there were "crows holding a convention in the cedars at the highest point of the island." The cedars were then a prominent feature of the Staten Island landscape. Thoreau had written that "the cedar seems to be one of the most common trees here, and the fields are fragrant with it." Davis noticed, however, that there were fewer crows coming than in years past. Today only an occasional crow is to be seen, and except for one isolated stand, the cedars have entirely succumbed to air pollution and urbanization.

*Weeping willow and boggy area, William T. Davis Wildlife
Refuge, Staten Island.*

Besides the crows there were many other now all-but-vanished birds. Of
the area where Great Kills Park is today, Davis wrote:

> *The beach-plums are a great attraction to a shore rambler, and
> the bay-berries to the white-breasted swallows that congregate
> on the Point in great flocks. . . . The branches of the bay
> often bend under their united weight, and the dark glossy blue
> of their backs make the group resplendent in color. . . . Mice
> are ever running in and out among the tussocks of grass, and
> the silent winged hawk steals upon them unawares. Then too,
> the great blue herons visit the unfrequented meadows, and stand
> sentinel there. . . . Many sandpipers run along the beach at
> certain seasons. . . . They look like little dancing machines,
> their movements are so rapid.*

In the 1920's Great Kills was used as a garbage dump; its marsh-and-shore ecology was destroyed and today it is a waste of phragmites reeds. The proposed shore drive from the Verrazano-Narrows Bridge to Tottenville will, if built, barricade the beach with a strip of concrete four hundred feet wide.

Like waves borne on a flood tide, the new housing developments keep breaking ground at ascending levels along the flanks of the central hills. With the redesignation of the Richmond Parkway route, the U-shaped greenbelt will be left mostly intact. Those who fought the battle of the greenbelt championed a cause that was not parochial but city wide, for within its series of linked open spaces High Rock Conservation Center and the William T. Davis Refuge are nature education laboratories to which over thirty-five thousand schoolchildren are bussed each year.

Not only children but Staten Island families and other metropolitan nature lovers come to these wildlife havens, particularly in the spring, to look for bright warblers in the newly clothed trees and to admire the

"Like waves borne on a flood tide, the new housing developments keep breaking ground at ascending levels along the flanks of the central hills."

woodland flowers: jack-in-the-pulpit, trout lily, Canada mayflower, may-apple, Solomon's seal (both true and false), spring beauty, swamp loose-strife. At High Rock the still air over the glacial ponds is broken by the deep guttural "thunk" of the green frog playing bass against the shrill counterpoint of the spring peepers. Stealthily a green heron or an occasional blue heron patrols these ponds. In the William T. Davis Refuge there are regiments of male redwing blackbirds, their handsome scarlet epaulets flashing as they fly through the marsh, while their shy brown-and-white-striped female mates, camouflaged in the cattail reeds nearby, search for food. Startled, a woodcock rises from her nest with a great whirring of wings. Watercress grows in the clear brook that winds through the refuge, and lovely large willows "weep" beside its banks. In all the moist places, beside the brook and where the old abandoned wells still send water percolating up out of the ground, the pungent-leaved skunk cabbage emits its unmistakable odor. On such a day it is natural to echo William T. Davis who, rejoicing in the coming of some bygone spring, wrote: "The world is indeed a wonderful place and it is good to be alive even if it is only for a little while, and more than half of us do not consider our natural surroundings seriously enough."

Certainly it is time to consider Staten Island's natural surroundings seriously, for now, inextricably, it has been sucked into the urban orbit, and soon the greenbelt will be like an island within an island, vestigially all that is left of the old Staten Island, the beautiful island beloved by Thoreau and Davis and Howard Cleaves. It will, we can only hope, remain inviolate from the depredations of private speculators and highway builders, and serve not just as an outdoor museum preserving Staten Island's ecological patrimony, but as a living laboratory of nature to nourish and educate us all.

Glacial pond, High Rock Conservation Center, Staten Island.

Woodcock, Staten Island.

Little green heron and nest, Staten Island.

Watercress and skunk cabbage growing in a brook, William T. Davis Wildlife Refuge, Staten Island.

7

MR. JOHNSON AND

JAMAICA BAY

Travelers circling over Kennedy Airport look down upon the Jamaica Bay Wildlife Refuge, a group of marshy islands with looping ribbons of water meandering through thick mats of cordgrass. They also see the long arm of the Rockaway Peninsula enclosing the bay and, in the center of the bay, the little community of Broad Channel, a strip town straddling Cross Bay Boulevard, where bungalows perch on stilts over the water and the principal landmark is the American Legion lodge.

Fifty thousand visitors come to the refuge each year, by car along Cross Bay Boulevard, or on the subway to Broad Channel station. Although the refuge is lovely in all seasons, its finest time is perhaps the autumn, when the pokeweeds turn a deep magenta and the scarlet rose hips of the *Rosa rugosa* gleam like balls on a Christmas tree. Pendant clusters of ripe red chokeberries and fronds of seaside goldenrod make bright splashes in the beach grass.

Herbert Johnson, the resident manager of the refuge, says, "I'll bet I've got the only bird sanctuary in the world with a subway running through it." And if transportation officials who would eviscerate the refuge by extending Kennedy Airport runways into the middle of the bay are permanently stayed in their plans, it may remain the only place where migratory birds and migratory people coexist in a curious truce.

Fortunately for Herbert Johnson and others who would preserve the wide airy expanse of the bay for conservation and recreation, a competing claim has been tendered by the U.S. Department of the Interior. In May 1969 Secretary of the Interior Walter Hickel announced a proposal for creating the Gateway National Recreation Area, embracing the entire New York Harbor with arms extending to Sandy Hook in New Jersey and the Rockaway Peninsula in New York. A team of officials studying the

Broad Channel, Jamaica Bay.

Jamaica Bay, "the only place where migratory birds and migratory people coexist in a curious truce."

Gateway proposal concluded that the seashore complex should include Jamaica Bay with its extraordinary wildlife refuge.

In colonial times, Jamaica Bay was considered the property of the free-holders of Jamaica, Long Island. The patent confirmation granted by Governor Nicolls in 1665 was for lands "to extend southeast to the Rock-away Swampe" from the early boundaries of the town. At an even earlier date, settlements had been built along the edge of the bay; in fact Flatlands, with its sea-level landscape like that of Holland, was established by the Dutch in 1636 and is the first known settlement on Long Island. Nearby Flatbush, known also by its Indian name of Midwout, was settled in 1651. In 1656 a patent was issued granting its "indwellers and inhabitants" the Canarsie meadows lying east of the Indian planting ground. These meadows were part of a system of salt marshes surrounding Jamaica Bay and were valuable for the salt hay they produced. The peripatetic Jasper Danckaerts described this scene:

There is towards the sea a large piece of low flat land which is overflowed at every tide, like the schorr *with us, miry and muddy at the bottom, and which produces a species of hard salt grass or reed grass. Such a place they call* valy *and mow it for hay, which cattle would rather eat than fresh hay or grass. . . . All the land from the bay to the Vlacke Bos [Flatbush] is low and level, and without the least elevation. . . . This marsh, like all the others, is well provided with good creeks which are navigable and very serviceable for fisheries. There is here a gristmill driven by the water which they dam up in the creek; and it is hereabouts they go mostly to shoot snipe and wild geese.*

An abundant livelihood was to be had from the sea, for another early journalist and prominent resident of the town of Jamaica, Daniel Denton, wrote: "Upon the South Side of Long Island in the winter, lie stores of Whales and Crampasses, which the inhabitants begin with small boats to make a trade Catching to their no small benefit. Also an innumerable multitude of seals, which make an excellent oyle; they lie all the Winter upon some broken Marshes and Beaches, or bars of sand."

The little Dutch towns and the English settlement at Gravesend eventually became part of the urban crust now covering southern Brooklyn and Queens. The mills that once stood beside the streams entering the bay have long since been replaced by the pollution control stations of the Department of Sanitation. Dikes and floodwalls constructed by the Army Corps of Engineers and the Shore Parkway built by Robert Moses have sealed off the tides that once inundated the extensive salt marshes around the perimeter of the bay, transforming the meadows where the cordgrasses were mowed for hay into a waving expanse of reeds. The wintering seals that lolled on the Rockaway beaches have been supplanted by summer crowds carrying transistor radios. The bay itself, however, has remained largely uninhabited, the place where the difficult problems of air traffic and sewage disposal have been allowed to fester. Ironically, Jamaica Bay, with its untapped potential both as a waterway and as a reclaimable landmass, has been the broad canvas on which city planners have attempted to paint some of their most visionary dreams.

In 1914 an ambitious scheme was advanced to dredge the bay and transform its eighteen thousand acres of water and marshlands into a huge industrial port and ship terminal. Proponents of the plan boasted that Jamaica Bay would then be greater than the combined ports of Liverpool, Rotterdam and Hamburg. As a start Canarsie Pier was built as a berth for oceangoing vessels, but the dredging project was abandoned, and Canarsie Pier became just a platform for fishermen.

As the age of air transport dawned, the flatlands on the margin of the bay were developed into runways and air terminals. Barren Island, which had been a sheep pasture and before that the hiding place of the pirate Gibbs's treasure trove, became Floyd Bennett Field, New York's first airport. Soon afterward, Flushing Meadow, on the north shore of Long Island, was filled in to create LaGuardia Airport, and in 1952 Floyd Bennett Field, no longer needed, was sold to the U.S. Navy. Then, as LaGuardia fast became overcrowded, Idlewild (now Kennedy) was created on the eastern perimeter of Jamaica Bay. The 4,527-acre tract of marshland, eight times the size of LaGuardia, was raised to a level twelve feet above high tide by dredging 53 million cubic yards of sand from the bay bottom. When Idlewild was completed in 1945, Mayor Fiorello LaGuardia said with characteristic punch, "I'm taking this opportunity to announce to the whole world that we have the best damn airport in the whole world."

Through the efforts of Parks Commissioner Moses the mayor had acquired nine thousand acres comprising the waters and islands of the bay plus three thousand acres of parkland on the perimeter of the bay. The manner in which Moses maneuvered this illustrates the tenacious qualities that made him New York's indomitable master builder for thirty years. In 1938, municipal warfare broke out between Moses and the Commissioner of Sanitation, who saw the low marshy lands of Jamaica Bay as a convenient dumping ground for the city's growing volume of refuse. Seizing the initiative, Moses countered this proposal with a plan of his own which he carried to the public in one of many brochures popularizing the works of his administration. An artist's sketch labeled "Civic Nightmare" depicted in lurid detail a mountain of smoking garbage covering the bay, its malodorous fumes wafting across Brooklyn and Queens. A second picture showed a blue expanse of water flecked with sailboats and fishing craft, its periphery rimmed with wide bathing beaches of white sand.

In one respect the Moses campaign was successful: state legislation was passed transferring Jamaica Bay to the jurisdiction of the Parks Department. Moses' scheme for turning the bay into a huge marine playground with "six new sparkling white beaches and green-shaded waterfront parks" is still pending, however. When Jamaica Bay became a park in 1938, its waters were considered unsafe for bathing. The newspapers which gave prominent coverage to Moses' visionary plan for a chain of Jamaica Bay beaches confidently announced that by the following year, under the harbor purification program of the Department of Public Works, the bay would be free of contamination. It was not. And the pollution of Jamaica Bay waters continues to mar every subsequent proposal for its recreational development.

During the long years when beach parks along the margins of the bay remained the dream of Moses and successive commissioners, another development was effected in the center of the bay which has proved of profound significance to bird watchers and nature lovers in New York City — the creation of Jamaica Bay Wildlife Refuge in 1951. The construction of the refuge was for Robert Moses an afterthought, the outgrowth of an accident. Where the subway now runs, a branch of the Long Island Railroad spanned the bay on a wooden trestle and carried passengers to the once elegant seaside resorts in the Rockaways. The trestle, built in 1877, would periodically catch fire, and in 1950 it was severely damaged by flames. The railroad decided to withdraw its service to the Rockaways, and the New York City Transit Authority agreed to purchase the old spur for its Rockaway line. Instead of rebuilding the trestle, the Transit Authority wanted to dredge sand from the bay to create an embankment on which to run its subway trains. Since the bay was a jealously guarded piece of Robert Moses' now considerable park empire, he refused to allow dredging for the subway embankment unless the Parks Department received something in return. It was agreed that in conjunction with its dredging operations, the Transit Authority would construct a series of dikes to impound fresh water. Two ponds, one on the east side of Cross Bay Boulevard, the other on the west, were thus created as an attraction to ducks and other waterfowl. By August 1953, the skeleton of the refuge was established.

Besides the ponds a nesting area was created on one of the larger islands in the bay, Canarsie Pol. The parks commissioner engineered another effort in interdepartmental cooperation by ordering that the organically rich sludge derived from the 26th Ward sewage treatment plant on the shore of Jamaica Bay be piped to Canarsie Pol. Canarsie Pol, at first only a barren stretch of sand protruding above the waters of the bay, soon became a fertile base for planting grass. After the sludge had been worked into the sandy surface to form a rich topsoil, tufts of beach grass and food plants were set out by Herbert Johnson. Before long Canarsie Pol was a grassy haven for nesting shorebirds.

At that time Jamaica Bay had a population of squatters — old-timers who lived in weather-beaten shacks perched over the water on wooden stilts — in a community called the Raunt. Artists frequently sketched the picturesque scene. The Raunt was reached by hiking from Cross Bay Boulevard across a rough road to a rickety wooden boardwalk which ran the length of the settlement.

Life at the Raunt was colorful but primitive. Water was collected in rain barrels and plumbing was nonexistent. There was electricity, a boon to Johnny Pasky's hotel, where there was, according to local account, "a real humdinger of a dance every Saturday night." Besides Pasky's, there were two other hotels for summer visitors: Smith's Run and Brorstrom's. The hotels and all the other decrepit structures that comprised the Raunt were ordered demolished by Moses at the time the refuge was created. Demolished too were the squatters' cabins that dotted the marsh grasses around Ruffle Bar.

The dispossessed old-time residents had only scorn for the new refuge and swore that the birds would ignore the two ponds. However, as the ponds collected rain and became almost like freshwater lakes, certain aquatic plants took hold: widgeon grass, muskgrass, and sago pondweed. And soon the birds did come, by the thousands. Migrant ducks that normally breed on the freshwater lakes and ponds of the prairie states — baldpates, pintails, gadwalls, ruddy ducks, green-winged teals — began to nest at Jamaica Bay along with the more common mallards, black ducks, and greater and lesser scaup. Brants came to graze on the sea lettuce that covered the bay bottom, and soon black skimmers and terns started to lay their eggs on the sand in the beach grass.

Jamaica Bay enjoys special prominence on the Atlantic flyway as a way station for migratory waterfowl, for the bay is the point of intersection of two separate migratory streams. Birds following the eastern coastline from Newfoundland, Nova Scotia and New Brunswick are joined at the bay by another group that breeds on the prairie ponds and lakes of Michigan and Canada. The refuge therefore has a unique geographical significance as the place of confluence for fall migrants and as the peeling-off point for birds headed north each spring. There are, in addition, many birds who stay and build their nests and raise their young in the protected reeds and grasses.

Perhaps the most remarkable thing about the wildlife sanctuary at Jamaica Bay is that it is not a natural but a re-created landscape, whose artful construction has been the lifework of one man — Herbert Johnson, a Parks Department employee for the past thirty-three years. A creative and gifted horticulturist, Johnson was appointed the resident superintendent of the refuge by Parks Commissioner Moses in 1951. Before coming to Jamaica Bay, he worked at a Parks Department soil-testing laboratory in

West Pond, Jamaica Bay.

the Bronx experimenting with the suitability of various types of grass for golf courses.

Johnson's horticultural apprenticeship began when he was a child watching and working with his father, an estate gardener. The refuge is Johnson's "estate," and in the tradition of his father he has managed it with skillful husbandry. But whereas his father labored to produce immaculately manicured lawns and well-cultivated flowerbeds, Herbert Johnson has worked to create the unkempt beauty of a seaside landscape.

Once the refuge was in operation, Johnson was left largely unsupervised to do as he pleased. From cuttings he gathered at other marine locations he propagated such berry-producing plants as autumn olive, *Rosa rugosa, Rosa multiflora,* bayberry and chokeberry. With seeds from pinecones which he took from Jacob Riis Park he started a nursery of Japanese black pines, later transplanting the seedlings in groves throughout the refuge. He also sowed wheat, oats and rye. The resulting wealth of grain, seeds and berries brought in many land birds to join the flourishing shorebird and waterfowl populations. In 1958, five years after the refuge was started, 208 species had been sighted at Jamaica Bay; the following year the count had climbed to 238; in 1960 it stood at 242 and by 1962 the tally was 283. Today the growing list is poised at 310.

There are an estimated two thousand bird watchers in New York City. Of this number about eight hundred get out regularly, and of these one hundred twenty are really good ornithologists. About twenty are absolute experts. Johnson is no inconsiderable expert himself. In the years he has lived at the refuge he has amassed a good ornithological library, and by patient observation he has stored up a tremendous amount of knowledge about bird behavior. Now his principal interest is involving the young in bird watching. School tours visit the refuge regularly, and Johnson takes time off from his other duties to conduct them around the mile-long triangular trail that skirts the West Pond.

Plans are under way to augment the educational function of the refuge by building an interpretive center. "When they get that thing going, it'll be great. The kids can see a good movie on water and birds and plants before they go out and see the real thing. It's going to make a big impression," says Johnson.

Of particular pride to the New York City bird watching community is

Glossy ibises, Jamaica Bay.

Snowy egrets, Jamaica Bay.

the return of the glossy ibis. For ninety years there had not been a single report of a glossy ibis in the area; then in 1961 three pairs nested in the Jamaica Bay Refuge. The following year their number had doubled, and today there are more than one hundred pairs.

The comeback of the snowy egret has been a cause of equal excitement. This bird with its billowing plumage was so prized by the feather trade that in 1923 it was pronounced extirpated. Fortunately, protective legislation had been passed by Congress a decade before, and by the 1930's the bird had made a miraculous resurrection. In 1960 two pairs nested at Jamaica Bay, and now, a decade later, a whole colony of these elegant birds with their long and angular necks have located their rookery on the banks of the West Pond.

Occasionally a bird very rare to the New York City range will appear at Jamaica Bay. When that happens, word goes out on the ornithological grapevine, and soon flocks of bird watchers converge on the refuge. Such an event occurred in February 1959, when a redwing thrush, the smallest of the European thrushes and one never before known to visit continental North America, was sighted. For several days the refuge swarmed with people who came to glimpse the eccentric visitor and record him on their life lists.

Another famous landing occurred on October 20, 1964, when a western pelican settled down on the West Pond. This huge bird with its nine-foot wingspread normally migrates diagonally from the northwestern United States to the Gulf of Mexico and Florida. Somehow blown off course, the pelican dropped down at the refuge that day with five snow geese, four blue geese and a peregrine falcon.

The success of the Jamaica Bay Refuge has not been unqualified, for there are a few birds, such as the osprey, that have resisted Herbert Johnson's hospitality. Actually, this is less the fault of the refuge management than of the deteriorating environment, which is having a particularly pernicious influence on the large birds of prey. Ospreys, once numerous on Long Island, have now limited their habitat to the eastern reaches of Suffolk County. DDT and other pesticides are responsible for their decline, for when sprayed on crops, they enter into the food chains of the smaller insects and animals, and through runoff they permeate the waters of the sea, infecting the fish. The lethal buildup is such that by the time

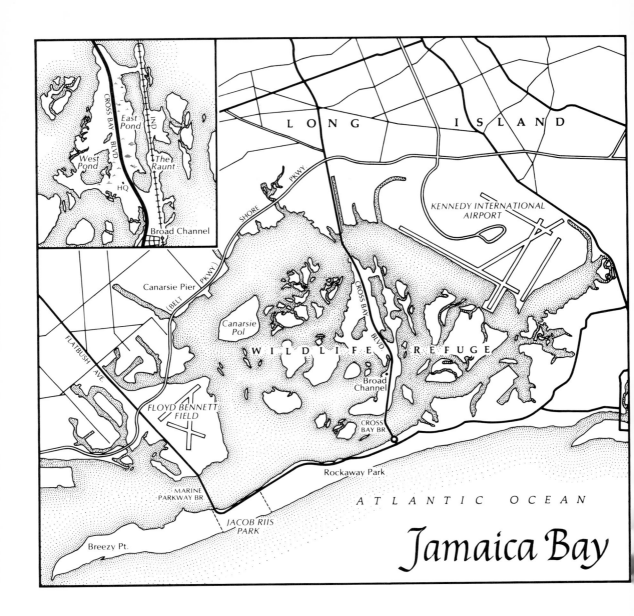

LONG ISLAND

KENNEDY INTERNATIONAL
AIRPORT

SHORE PKWY

CROSS BAY PKWY

(BELT PKWY)

FLATBUSH AVE

Canarsie Pier

Canarsie
Pol

W I L D L I F E   R E F U G E

CROSS BAY BLVD

Broad
Channel

FLOYD BENNETT
FIELD

CROSS
BAY BR

Rockaway Park

MARINE
PARKWAY BR

JACOB RIIS
PARK

Breezy Pt.

A T L A N T I C   O C E A N

Jamaica Bay

CROSS BAY BLVD

East
Pond

IND

West
Pond

The
Raunt

HQ

Broad Channel

the ospreys or other carnivorous birds catch a fish or meadow mouse, the intake of poison is sufficient to cause reproductive failure or what the scientists refer to as the thin-eggshell phenomenon — eggs that collapse when the bird tries to incubate them.

The bald eagle has been victimized in this way. These eagles must once have been numerous around Jamaica Bay, and they must have held special significance for the Indians, because the confirmatory deed to the settlers of the township of Jamaica contains this proviso: "One thing to be remembered, that noe person is to cut downe any tall trees wherein eagles doe build their nests." Herbert Johnson says that for the past three years in the dead of winter, usually between Christmas and New Year's, he has seen a lone eagle appear at the refuge for a few days.

On March 1, 1962, a calamity occurred when an American Airlines 707 jet bound for Los Angeles with ninety-five persons aboard lifted off the runway at Kennedy Airport and then suddenly plummeted into the waters of Jamaica Bay in a burst of flames. For days the refuge was overrun with heavy machinery and emergency personnel as firemen retrieved the dismembered bodies that were scattered in the water and all over the marsh. Among the peripheral losses of the tragedy were five hundred acres of beach grass, five hundred *Rosa rugosa,* two hundred Japanese black pines and ten red cedars. Johnson soon began replanting the scarred acres, and before long nature, with its sublime indifference to human fate, had eradicated all signs of the disaster.

Today the life of the refuge itself is threatened by airplanes. Passenger traffic at New York's three major airports has grown tenfold over the last twenty years. In 1970, 45 million people took air trips; this number will double by 1980. For years transportation officials have been requesting the construction of a fourth jetport, but New York and New Jersey politicians have been deadlocked over the issue as opposition from local conservation groups has mounted. One at least partial answer to the problem would be to fill in the eastern half of Jamaica Bay and build additional runways at Kennedy.

Such a plan was proposed by the Port Authority, and a team of consultants representing the National Academy of Sciences was hired to assess the consequences of the Kennedy expansion. It held that more runways would undoubtedly be harmful to the ecology of the bay. Expansion of

Kennedy Airport would almost certainly destroy the refuge and ruin the recreation potential of Jamaica Bay. Additional runways would inhibit tidal flushing action within the bay, already weakened by previous encroachments, and thereby water pollution would be increased. The added petrochemical waste discharge from the airport would compound the pollution. Even if the new construction left a portion of the refuge intact, there would perhaps exist the need to eliminate the birds as a hazard to flight operations.

Herbert Johnson's expansive smile fades as he surveys the two ponds with their teeming birdlife and the beautiful marine landscape — his life's work spread out before him — and thinks of the airplanes. Though he is eligible for retirement, he says he has no plans for leaving the refuge. He vows, "I'll stay here until I wake up some morning and find an airplane sitting over there in the parking lot."

Greater egret, Jamaica Bay.

8

ISLAND OF DESPAIR,

ISLAND OF PROMISE

They named it Welfare back in 1921 to erase its notoriety, the island called Blackwell's, whose Black Maria had once trundled the city's insane, indigent, outlawed and outcast from its ferry landing to those austere institutions: the asylum, the almshouse and the penitentiary. It is a stony bar two miles long and eight hundred feet wide bisecting the East River into two channels opposite the area between Forty-eighth Street and Eighty-sixth Street in Manhattan. The treacherous currents of Hell Gate swirl around its northern tip. It is, with the exception of one area in Long Island City, the most southerly appearance aboveground of the city's most ancient bedrock formation, Fordham gneiss.

Now with its decayed, weed-encroached buildings, as silent and provocative as the ruins of a vanished civilization, it exudes a ghostliness. But alongside the relics of the past, future-shaping forces are at work. Today an army of hard hats occupies the island: one battalion is boring a

Blackwell's Island, as represented in a Currier & Ives Lithograph, 1862.

large distribution station for a new city water tunnel; another is digging for the Sixty-third Street subway tube that will plug the island into the rest of New York City.

The wings of the old lunatic asylum have been amputated, leaving its beautiful domed central octagon prominently silhouetted against the sky. A flat brick-scattered plain marks the site of the old almshouse; an occasional weather-beaten wheelchair lies rusting on the premises, a souvenir of its past as a place of last resort for the aged and disabled.

For several months the demolition men have been priming the canvas upon which planners and builders operating under the direction of Edward Logue of the New York State Urban Development Corporation will paint a new landscape, a new town called Island Town. The debris-strewn island is also the slate upon which plans are being drawn for five new parks, the largest of which is to be a twenty-five-acre ecological park operated by the State Park Commission for the City of New York.

The overall plan for Welfare Island was drawn up by Philip Johnson and John Burgee and presented to the city in October 1969. Several well-known architectural and landscape architectural firms are now participating in the design of the various components of that plan. Funds from a variety of government housing subsidy programs will provide five thousand apartments for people whose incomes range from poverty level to affluent.

Private automobiles entering the island will be funneled into a giant garage; circulation around the island will be by minitransit or on foot. The now decrepit Blackwell farmhouse, one of the last remaining specimens of eighteenth-century architecture in New York City, will be restored as the focal point of a park separating the new town's two high-density development clusters. A continuous promenade will rim the waterfront. The island's two functioning hospitals will remain in existence. Basically, then, the Welfare Island of the future will consist of activity nodes — its present medical institutions, plus new housing, shopping, and entertainment complexes that are lively and intensely urban — interspersed with five quiet zones for recreation and relaxation.

The ecological park, called Octagon Park after its principal landmark, will be programmed to create certain kinds of environmental awareness. The architect, Dan Kiley, wants in his design of the park to articulate certain timeless relationships between human beings and their environment. He is interested in the ways in which man has measured and ordered nature, in man's methods of comprehending and defining such things as gravity, air, light, water. He would like to create a kind of outdoor architecture that will help explain these elemental and universal forces that shape and govern human life. One Kiley proposal is for a "geology ecocenter" — an amphitheater-like bowl bored out of the island's Fordham gneiss bedrock. Tiered seats on one side would face a cascading sheet of water; a shaft positioned in the center of the bowl would act as a giant sundial marking the hours and the shifting direction of light throughout the day.

Conservation-minded critics of the Urban Development Corporation's plan would ban new development on Welfare Island altogether. "The whole island should become a park," they say. "Twenty-five acres for an ecological park that is supposed to serve one million schoolchildren is a joke." They are right. Twenty-five acres *is* too small an area for a park if that park is to be a significant and representative remnant of the city's pre-urban ecology. The conservationists miss the point, however. Such a re-

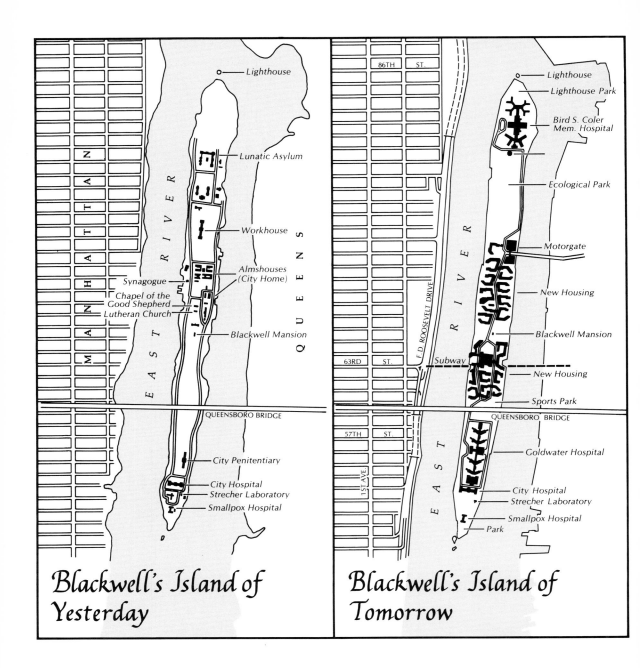

Blackwell's Island of Yesterday

- Lighthouse
- Lunatic Asylum
- Workhouse
- Almshouses (City Home)
- Synagogue
- Chapel of the Good Shepherd
- Lutheran Church
- Blackwell Mansion
- City Penitentiary
- City Hospital
- Strecher Laboratory
- Smallpox Hospital

MANHATTAN

EAST RIVER

QUEENS

QUEENSBORO BRIDGE

Blackwell's Island of Tomorrow

86TH ST.

- Lighthouse
- Lighthouse Park
- Bird S. Coler Mem. Hospital
- Ecological Park
- Motorgate
- New Housing
- Blackwell Mansion
- Subway
- New Housing
- Sports Park

63RD ST.

F.D. ROOSEVELT DRIVE

EAST RIVER

QUEENSBORO BRIDGE

57TH ST.

1ST AVE.

- Goldwater Hospital
- City Hospital
- Strecher Laboratory
- Smallpox Hospital
- Park

Blackwell's Island of Yesterday

Blackwell's Island of Tomorrow

creation of the past would be impossible in this case, even if the whole island were devoted to park purposes. By its size and location Welfare Island is precluded from duplicating the Jamaica Bay feat of coaxing back into existence the native plant endowment; it is 147 acres compared to Jamaica Bay's 9,150 acres, and unlike Jamaica Bay it is not situated on the perimeter of the great city, but at its center.

Perhaps the lesson that Welfare Island has to offer is not a conservation lesson, but a planning lesson. If successfully carried to completion along lines proposed, it will become something more than the sum of its parts — although individually these parts may be very attractive, since they represent the greatest concentration of top-level professional talent in a single area in the city's history. The superaddition here will be a humanistically conceived environment for living. To think of another such intelligent community planning effort in this city one must go back to the 1911 plan for Forest Hills Gardens — recent attempts such as Co-op City having ended up as nothing more than vastly distended housing projects.

Implicit in the overall plan for Welfare Island is a sense of romance, and if it is anything, Welfare Island is romantic: romantic in its insularity, like the Ile de la Cité in Paris a river-bound sliver in the heart of a great city; romantic in its almost postcard panorama of the Manhattan skyline; romantic in the brutalistic sense, with its views of the powerful industrial scenery of Queens and the great girders and trusses of the Queensboro Bridge soaring overhead.

But Welfare Island's romance is more than topographical; it is historical too. Even from the beginning of colonial times, when the Dutch called it Varcken (Hog) Island because swine were pastured there, the island was a place of exile. Bought in 1637 from the Indians by the Dutch governor Wouter Van Twiller for a country estate, it was transferred to the British crown in 1664 and in 1668 granted to Captain John Manning, then sheriff of New York. Manning fell into disgrace when, acting as commander of the fort during the absence of Governor Lovelace in 1673, he hastily surrendered to the Dutch, who had staged a naval assault to regain control of their old colony. Manning's incensed fellow townsmen charged treason, and although he made a pilgrimage to England to explain his actions to King James II, who exonerated him, they nonetheless court-martialed him upon his return, and finding him guilty, banished him to his island. His

banishment, like that of Boss Tweed, who two centuries later, in 1871, also paid his dues on the island for besmirching the city's honor, was not entirely painful. Manning lived in a fine mansion dubbed "the castle" and entertained his visitors with bowls of rum punch.

The site of Manning's "castle" — at the southern end of the island opposite Turtle Bay (today the UN) — was also the site of Tweed's home on the island, the city penitentiary. Designed by James Renwick, architect of the Smithsonian Institution, with a nostalgic eye toward medieval dungeons, the penitentiary also resembled a castle, with rounded turrets and a roof profile of notched battlements. Tweed supposedly had a picture window cut into one wall so that he could better view the city he had swindled.

Between the time of Manning's exile and the purchase of the island by the city in 1828 as a likely place to quarantine its convicts, the island passed through several bucolic generations in the hands of the Blackwell family. The first Blackwell was Robert, who married Captain Manning's stepdaughter and heir. Their grandson, Jacob Blackwell, was the proprietor of the island during the Revolutionary War, when the island figured only marginally in the tumult swirling all around it. British troops, following their victory on Long Island, landed on Blackwell's Island, but they were immediately repulsed by rebel cannon shot fired from the batteries located on Manhattan. In 1782 a British officer inspecting the prison ships made the compassionate suggestion that the prisoners should be allowed on Blackwell's Island during the daytime in the hot season, but it is not known whether this recommendation was carried out.

Jacob Blackwell's sons were bequeathed the island in 1780. Finding themselves in financial trouble following the war, they put it up for sale. The advertisement that appeared in Loudon's *New York Packet* in March 1784 describes its scenery at that period:

For Sale, that pleasant agreeably situated Island, known by the
name of
BLACKWELL'S ISLAND,
On the East River, about four miles from this city.

Site of the old almshouse, Blackwell's Island.

It is without exception one of the most healthy situations in this state. It is remarkable for the number of fish and fowl that is caught there in the different seasons. There is on the premises, two small Dwelling Houses, a Barn, Bake and Fowl House, Cyder Mill; a large Orchard, containing 450 of the best grafted fruit trees, such as Newton & golden pippins, spitsinburghs, peirmans, bow apples, pears, peaches, plumbs, cherries, &c. There is a number of the best stone quarries, ready cleared to begin breaking immediately; and the subscriber has a complete set of quarry tools, with all his farming utensils and stock to dispose of at the same time. The Island abounds with running springs of most excellent water. The above contains 107 acres, eight of which are a salt meadow, and the whole has been considerably improved with manure, and in good fence.

A buyer was not found and so the property remained in the hands of Blackwell heirs until the city purchased it. Not long after that the old quarries were being worked by convict labor, and soon the banded gray gneiss was transformed into what one nineteenth-century newspaper ac-

Aerial view of Blackwell's Island in the 1930's, showing the penitentiary designed by James Renwick (now demolished).

Convicts quarrying rocks, Blackwell's Island, circa 1890.

count characterized as "a little city on the waters . . . a city in which all the misery, despair and viciousness of the metropolis are epitomized."

A vivid description of the island with its Victorian penal and medical institutions was penned by Charles Dickens who, with his penchant for documenting human wretchedness, made a point of visiting Blackwell's Island in 1842 during his travels in this country. In his *American Notes* he wrote that at the northern end of the island he saw the lunatic asylum where "the terrible crowd with which these halls and galleries were filled, so shocked me, that I abridged my stay within the shortest possible limits. . . . The moping idiot, cowering down with long dishevelled hair; the gibbering maniac, with his hideous laugh and pointed finger; the vacant eye, the fierce wild face, the gloomy picking of the hands and lips, and munching of the nails: there they were all, without disguise, in naked ugliness and horror."

The almshouse with its long segregated dormitories and workrooms impressed him "very uncomfortably," while the penitentiary at the southern end of the island — that battlemented, turreted fortress where Tweed

was later imprisoned — inspired his compassionate ire. To conjure up an adequate impression of the place he suggests: "Make the rain pour down, outside in torrents. Put the everlasting stove in the midst; hot and suffocating, and vaporous, as a witch's caldron. Add a collection of gentle odours, such as would arise from a thousand mildewed umbrellas, wet through, and a thousand buck-baskets, full of half-washed linen — and there is the prison as it was that day."

The lunatic asylum, its octagonal rotunda built in the Greek Revival style, is considered to be the work of the architect A. J. Davis. Admired by Dickens for its "spacious and elegant staircase," it has been praised by the architectural historian Henry Russell Hitchcock as being "as generous in scale and as interesting for the original sort of handling of space as a Baroque stair hall." He says, "It is the grandest interior in the City dating from before the Grand Central Station concourse and a fascinating premonition of the Guggenheim Museum that Wright certainly never saw!" The original building was begun in 1835 and completed in 1839. That same year a long west wing was added; and in 1848 another long wing was built to the south. These wings where self-anointed scepter bearers once hallucinated are now lopped off, and their rubble has been combined with the excavated debris from the new subway tunnel as landfill at the island's southern end. Gone too are the asylum's auxiliary buildings, the Lodge, where the most violent inmates were kept, and the Retreat, for female patients, of whom there were usually twice as many as males.

Although Dickens was doubtless rightfully horrified at the conditions assigned mental patients of that pre-psychiatric era, there was an innocent charm at least in their external surroundings. The asylum grounds (site of the new ecological park) were shaded by tall willows, horse chestnuts and buttonwoods and adorned with an ornamental summerhouse and an ice skating pond (which also provided block ice for the asylum and the nearby almshouse). A carriage road arched by trees led to the sail-flecked water. The view to the east was of Ravenswood in Queens — not the Ravenswood of today with Consolidated Edison's three giant smokestacks looming against the sky, but a Ravenswood of "luxuriant foliage and elegant architecture," in the words of one nineteenth-century journalist. From the opposite side of the island the view of the Manhattan shore with its "noble mansions and their boat houses" was equally agreeable. Twenty

The staircase of the old lunatic asylum, Blackwell's Island, "the grandest interior in the City dating from before the Grand Central Station concourse . . ."

The "Octagon" from the exterior, Blackwell's Island.

acres of land adjoining the asylum were given over to a vegetable garden, and there was an extensive flower garden as well.

At the far tip of the island where the lighthouse now stands there was a curious structure known as Maxey's Fort. It was built of blocks of clay and grass dug from the marsh behind it. According to accounts of the day it was built soon after the Civil War by a mad army officer of Irish descent, Thomas Maxey, and mounted with a wooden cannon. Fearing an invasion by rebel privateers, Maxey would stand guard each day brandishing a wooden bayonet on a broom handle. In spite of this warriorlike attitude, however, he was a gentle person, and extremely fond of birds. An elaborate gate decorated the causeway that led over the salt marsh to the fort; it had two large openings near the top designed by Maxey to accommodate the nests of wild geese. Inscribed upon it were these words:

I INVITE THE FOWLS

AND THE BIRDS OF THE AIR

TO ENTER

134

Beside the fort Maxey had built himself a little thatched-roof house over which giant hollyhocks and sunflowers towered. At first the directors of the asylum were entirely approving, since through his labors Maxey was able to make an effective contribution toward draining the marsh. Later, however, they decided that the ramshackle fort had to make way for the present lighthouse. According to some accounts Maxey was persuaded to demolish the fort and build the lighthouse himself. The inscription at the base of the lighthouse, however, reads:

THIS IS THE WORK

WAS DONE BY

JOHN MC CARTHY

WHO BUILT THE LIGHT

HOUSE FROM THE BOTTOM TO THE

TOP ALL YE THAT DO PASS BY MAY

PRAY FOR HIS SOUL WHEN HE DIES

It would seem, then, either that "Thomas Maxey" was a fictitious name or that John McCarthy was another lunatic-craftsman or a prisoner or alms-house resident excused from the normal routine to build the lighthouse. It is unclear whether he worked from a blueprint or designed the lighthouse himself.

Today the area reserved for Island Town's motorgate, or automobile depository, is a desolate yet strangely beautiful wasteland. A little vine-enshrouded bandstand and a broken flagpole bearing a mosaic of Fiorello LaGuardia are the only remains of the City Home that once occupied this part of the island. Where its collection of ramshackle old buildings have been most recently torn down the ground is sterile, studded with bricks and debris, but where the buildings have been gone for a few years a luxuriant meadow of weeds and wildflowers and sapling trees has sprung up.

Originally the city's vagrants and helpless poor were incarcerated with hardened criminals in the Tombs and the penitentary. The alms-house, also known as the workhouse and the house of correction, was built out of the readily available gray Fordham gneiss shortly after the city acquired the island in 1828. Although its administrators still adhered

The lighthouse, Blackwell's Island.

to the "poverty is a crime" philosophy, the almshouse humanized to some degree the plight of the poor. After 1850 there was discrimination between the aged and disabled — inmates of the almshouse — and the able-bodied indigents — assigned to the workhouse — although technically both groups belonged to the same institution. According to a journalist, W. H. Davenport, who contributed his impressions of Blackwell's Island to *Harper*'s magazine in 1866, the workhouse was designed by the city commissioners to be "as repulsive as is consistent with humanity," while the almshouse was supposed to be "a place of comparative comfort, liberally though economically maintained." In the beginning a modest stipend was given to workhouse laborers. This practice was soon dropped, however, as the workhouse became an exclusively penal institution for minor offenders — persons convicted of small thefts, drunkenness, vagrancy, or disorderly conduct.

136

These petty criminals and social transgressors were maintained by the city's taxpayers at the rate of fifteen cents per person per day; their labor, which was contracted out to city manufacturers, brought in approximately six thousand dollars a year. Workhouse laborers produced such things as cigars, uniforms for Union soldiers and hoopskirt forms. Most of the articles they made, however, were for institutional consumption on the island. The superintendent's report dated December 31, 1851, enumerates the tin basins, cups, pails, washtubs, iron bedsteads, coal boxes, wheelbarrows, ox yokes and coffins (2,628) produced during the preceding twelve months.

In 1869 male and female blind asylums were added to the almshouse-workhouse complex, and the entire institution was named the New York City Home for Aged and Infirm. "The blind leading the blind" became a common and poignant sight as each morning a line would form of men two abreast, arms touching the shoulders in front, to be led to the barber shop.

The ranks of the inmates would swell every year as winter approached and seasonal labor was laid off; no one was ever turned away, and so the City Home was continually crowded beyond capacity. Things were so bad at the end of the nineteenth century that people were sleeping two and three to a bed as well as on the floors, in an outdoor shed and even in tents. There was in spite of this a serenity and a quiet village beauty about the place with its carefully tended flowerbeds, grassplots and hedges.

Certain improvements in the living conditions at the City Home were eventually introduced. In 1929 china dishes replaced tin cups and plates. Following his appointment in 1934 as Hospitals Commissioner during the administration of LaGuardia, Dr. S. S. Goldwater issued a genteelly phrased set of rules decreeing that the inmates be referred to as "guests" and that they in turn observe the following standards: "cleanliness, conduct becoming ladies and gentlemen and regard for one another's property." Prior to this the "guests'" property — sums earned from the sale of brooms and baskets — had been ruthlessly embezzled by the wardens of the City Home. Besides reforming its administration, Goldwater also carried out a program of modernization of the City Home's antiquated, non fireproof facilities. In 1952 the 124-year history of the Blackwell's Island almshouse came to an end. Its able-bodied inmates were transferred to the Staten Island farm colony, and those that were bedridden were placed in the newly opened Bird S. Coler Hospital, at the north end of the Island. Bird S. Coler and Goldwater, at the south end of the island, are both city-operated hospitals for the chronically ill, mostly aged paralytics. Excluded from normal society by their infirmities, from private nursing homes by their budgets, and, in some cases, from their homes by relatives, the patients move in wheelchairs up and down hospital corridors and, on fine days, outside, where they warm themselves in the sunshine, braced by the East River breeze and the scenic Manhattan profile. Various therapy programs help to fill their days.

These two hospitals, the successors to a number of other now defunct public hospitals on the island, will be retained within the framework of the new town plan. Some of the old hospital structures are being saved as landmarks; they are reminders of the island's role as a place of quarantine in those prevaccine days when various contagious diseases struck terror into the hearts of city dwellers. Tuberculosis patients were put in the old lunatic asylum building after it became the Metropolitan Hospital in 1894. From 1902 to 1921 the building also housed a leper colony.

The Smallpox Hospital, called the "pest-house," was designed by James Renwick in 1854. It is now a crumbling hulk at the southern end of the island. Its battlemented roof line once echoed that of Renwick's now demolished penitentiary.

There were other grimly named hospitals for the contagious which have now vanished: Fever Hospital, Paralytic Hospital, Scarlet Fever Hospital. Then there was City Hospital, once characterized as "a great gray temple to disease." Built in 1858 out of gneiss quarried on the island after a fire destroyed the original wood-frame hospital, it was abandoned in 1957 and is now a vandal-ravaged ruin used by the Fire Department training school for wall-scaling practice. Nearby is the neo-Renaissance Strecher Laboratory, built in 1892, where morbid scavengers can still find the pickled organs of long-dead patients.

So imbued was the island with the atmosphere of disease and death that in the minds of many a trip across the East River was synonymous with a trip across the River Styx. For many others, of course, a trip across the East River was not to a hospital bed but to a prison cell, and eventually

The female almshouse, Blackwell's Island.

the island gained much more notoriety from its prison than from its hospitals.

Within the turreted Victorian fortress in which Boss Tweed had served time so comfortably (where Goldwater Hospital now stands) Mae West was sentenced to spend ten days in 1921 for her "indecent performance" in a play called *Sex*. What galled her most was exchanging her skintight gold gown for a prison issue dress and the itchy underwear of which she complained bitterly for the duration of her stay. She even wrote a poem on the subject to the warden; captivated, he later recalled her as "just a wholesome woman trying to serve ten days."

There were prison riots at the penitentiary in the 1930's. The worst, that of October 23, 1932, was triggered off by a feud between the Italian and Irish gangs who were competing for influence within the prison. But soon afterward, not only had the gangs healed their differences, they were partners in the operation of a vice ring that embraced the entire penitentiary. Joe Rao, a Harlem gangster, bootlegger and racketeer, who had been convicted of extortion in the Bronx soda water trade, headed the Italian faction. Edward Cleary was the Irish leader. They lived with their henchmen in different hospital wards in the manner of feudal barons, smoking expensive cigars and wearing silk shirts and underwear and costly dressing gowns.

Their control over the prison was absolute; even the guards assisted in the sale of narcotics to the inmates. Heroin was brought into the prison by carrier pigeon. Cleary maintained his pigeon cote in a hospital room; Rao had a cote built for his birds on the roof of a storehouse. Steaks and other choice foods were stolen from the prison commissary, and the gang lords were served in their rooms by valets.

Like partners in an ingenious syndicate, Rao and Cleary were able to squeeze a profit out of practically every aspect of prison life. The clothes of the new inmates were confiscated and sold; privileges — jobs easier or potentially more lucrative — were sold. Even the warden's parole list was presented to Rao and Cleary for approval.

On January 24, 1934, as one of the first acts of his administration, the Little Flower had his newly appointed Commissioner of Corrections, Austin McCormick, stage a predawn raid on the prison. Rao and Cleary and their henchmen were ousted from their comfortable hospital dormitories and marched to the most unpleasant cells in the prison. All of the other cells were cleared and their contents were thrown into the hallways — handkerchiefs soaked in a heroin solution, files, razors, pieces of lead pipe, and, from one section of the prison, transvestite trappings — cosmetics, perfume, female underwear, and a lady's wig. The prison's depravity, beforehand rumored but now fully exposed, led to renewed demands that it be replaced by a new prison on Riker's Island, and in 1936 the infamous old stone fortress on Welfare Island was demolished.

A hot debate soon arose within the city administration over the future use of the old prison site. With a typical flair for public relations, Parks Commissioner Robert Moses immediately published plans for a new sports park. Hospitals Commissioner Goldwater argued the case for a new hospital for the chronically ill, and eventually his side prevailed and the hospital that today bears his name was constructed in 1939.

Mixed among the island's penal, medical and charity institutions were several churches which, with the construction of interior chapels in Goldwater and Bird S. Coler hospitals, were allowed to fall into disuse. The largest, a Catholic church serving the residents of the City Home, has been demolished. The little synagogue beside it, built in 1928 and now abandoned except for a residential wing occupied by the rabbi who is a chaplain at Bird S. Coler, is slated for demolition. Scheduled to remain as a landmark in the plan for Island Town is the Church of the Good Shepherd, a Victorian Gothic structure designed by Frederick Clark Withers and built in 1889 at a cost of eighty thousand dollars. Its fine stone carving and handsome interior woodwork are witness to the nineteenth-century Christian attitude that though the indigent should live in harshness and discomfort they should nonetheless worship in beauty. The church is maintained by the Episcopal Mission Society, and its basement serves as the home of the Protestant chaplain of Bird S. Coler, a scholarly ex-missionary to Liberia. Two other defunct churches, one Episcopalian, one Catholic, also house hospital chaplains.

A little Lutheran church next to the Church of the Good Shepherd, in which services once were conducted in German, is crumbling into ruins. Sunlight pours through its broken roof, its floorboards are gradually rotting away. Standing there, one wonders what would happen if the entire city like this little church were abandoned. Without people transforming, subduing, reconstructing the natural world there would be only nature's own relentless dynamic at work, and soon New York would become some eerily impressive, vegetation-encased North American version of Angkor Wat. Of course this won't happen, at least not yet. But Welfare Island, part of the city yet at a remove from it, the eye of the hurricane, as it were, is a good vantage point from which to speculate about the relationship between nature and the urban machine. The message the new ecological park might impart is that nature is not something "out there" away from the city, but a force within — governed by, but at the same time governing, the lives of the inhabitants.

CONCLUSION

E. B. White once wrote a book about New York City. At the time he wrote it, the dawning consciousness of the presence of the hydrogen bomb in the world underlined in absolute terms for the first time in history man's potential for self-destruction. As an antidote to the bomb, White chose the symbol of a tree, a tree growing in the garden of an old townhouse at Turtle Bay near the home of the then newly formed United Nations.

A block or two west of the new City of Man in Turtle Bay there is an old willow tree that presides over an interior garden. It is a battered tree, long suffering and much climbed, held together by strands of wire but beloved of those who know it. In a way it symbolizes the city: life under difficulties, growth against odds, sap-rise in the midst of concrete, and the steady reaching for the sun. Whenever I look at it nowadays, and feel

143

the cold shadow of the planes, I think: "This must be saved, this particular thing, this very tree." If it were to go, all would go — this city, this mischievous and marvellous monument which not to look upon would be like death.

The city and the tree, existing not in opposition but in conjunction; the tree a living thing in an artificial world, not an optional amenity, but an absolute necessity. By extension, New York's forests and wetlands are absolute necessities. Now besides the fear of nuclear holocaust, people are beginning to experience the new fear of "ecotastrophe," an environment so mindlessly polluted that it becomes unfit for habitation.

In a scenario for a city struck by ecotastrophe, besides an atmospheric soup of toxic gasses and waters slimy with oil and poisonous with chemicals and reeking with effluvia, there would be a barren, treeless, vegetationless landscape. By contrast, a scenario for a healthy city would include green and living things within the urban fabric — not just street trees and garden trees, important as these may be, but living forests and wetlands functioning as intact ecosystems. "In wildness is preservation of the world," wrote Henry David Thoreau. A modern-day version of his dictum might read: "In parks are preservation of the city."

Without exception, the salvaging from development and despoilation of the forests and the wetlands discussed in this book rest upon the victories of concerned citizens and city officials who have understood that a city without trees would not be a city worth living in. They understood too, since New York is in its way as much of a water city as Venice — "the city of nested-in bays," Walt Whitman called it — that to lack an accessible shorefront (accessible to people, not just automobiles) would be an almost equal impoverishment. It is remarkable, really, that during the last century, a period of tremendous urban growth, there were visionaries who knew these things: knew that New York City in its relentless march uptown, erasing its native endowment, straight-jacketing itself within the rigidity of a grid plan, would, for its own future benefit, have to withhold from development some parcels of the patriarchial ecology.

It is not accidental that the park movement in the United States coincided with the Industrial Revolution. The growth of capital made possible substantial public improvements. Cities emulated and competed with each

144

other in the realm of civic grandeur; parks, like opera houses, became emblems of cultural pride. The Industrial Revolution gave birth to a leisure class, and the new parks like Central Park and Prospect Park became the city's playgrounds, the places to see and be seen. The immigrant labor attracted to this country by the employment opportunities of the Industrial Revolution became a ready reserve corps for various public works projects including the laying out and maintenance of new parks. As the leaders of the Industrial Revolution in America put up big estates on the banks of the Hudson and the shores of Long Island Sound, they imported as groundkeepers European gardeners, many of whom later transferred their services to the Parks Department. The Industrial Revolution also spurred the growth of slums, and this led to the birth in the second half of the nineteenth century of a new humanitarianism. The creation of parks like Pelham Bay Park were seen as means to ameliorate the lives of the working class, whose otherwise drudgery-filled days were spent in factories, sweatshops and cramped tenements. Too, this was the age of romanticism, when nature was regarded as salubrious, a physical tonic and a moral inspiration.

Whereas in England the parks had their genesis as private playgrounds for princes, American parks were from their beginning public places, democratic in spirit. The nineteenth-century parks were designed for yet another purpose: edification. This was the period in which zoos and botanical gardens were born, and parks like the great one in the Bronx were created to house them. In like spirit the American Museum of Natural History was founded in 1870 to further scientific exploration and to assemble wildlife and archaeological specimens from the four corners of the world.

Everyday rural nature was then still part of the daily context for most New Yorkers. There was a dairy in Central Park as well as a sheepfold (now the Tavern on the Green); sheep grazed on the sheep meadow as late as 1934. In the nineteenth century there was no need for the ersatz barnyards — our twentieth-century version of romanticism, edification with a Walt Disney twist — that we build for today's rurally disposed city children, for whom a cow is practically as exotic as a tiger.

How do the twentieth-century park planners score by comparison with the open-space visionaries of the nineteenth? The doughty, much embattled emperor of the city's Parks Department for so many years, Robert Moses, has been both ardently praised and ardently castigated for his contributions to the city's park system. Credit for the creation of various bathing beaches and the salvation of Jamaica Bay belong to him. Still, he is a "facilities-oriented" rather than a "nature-oriented" man, and the nineteenth-century park legacy suffered when he incised it with highways and encroached upon it with barricaded, asphalt-surfaced playgrounds. The waterfront suffered too under Moses because of a misbegotten notion that for twentieth-century man the highest form of recreational pleasure was driving a car; today sixty-three miles of city waterfront are flanked by a concrete cordon of drives. True, these drives are combined in many places with waterfront promenades, but, except where the two are separated vertically, as in Brooklyn Heights or the John Jay Walk in Carl Shurz Park in Manhattan, the noise and fumes make the pedestrian experience so unappealing that the promenades are generally avoided.

It would be unfair to assign Moses too much blame for the prevailing attitude toward open space in New York City, an attitude that regards all open space, even public parks (which should have at least a semblance of inviolability) as land banks, up for grabs whenever the urgency for housing or a school or a police station or fire station or a senior citizens center or whatever other worthy project becomes great enough. These bids for development are constantly being tendered by well-meaning public servants representing the interests of various municipal agencies, by politicians with promises to keep, by philanthropists. New York is still a growing city, and vacant land is getting scarcer and more expensive all the time. To some of the parks I have discussed, this book may be a sentimental salute, a nostalgic goodbye before they are erased or altered — altered not by the march of progress, for nobody believes anymore that we are on a course of inexorable material betterment, but altered rather by change and uncaring and too many people pressing their demands on too little land.

In the last analysis, whether a park stays or goes or a new one like the one on Welfare Island is built, the decision is a political one. For millions of years the size and shape and extent of the forests and wetlands of New York were decided solely by nature's own relentless dynamic: by encroaching or receding coastal waters, by the succession of plant communities responding to climatic change, by progressive topographical modifications wrought by wind and ice and water. Now, though these forces are still operative, there is added to the natural dynamic the urban dynamic, a dynamic of politically arrived at decisions concerning the way land gets used.

Take Jamaica Bay as a case in point — a classic textbook case, really — for Jamaica Bay is the last piece of the pie, the city's one remaining sizable reserve of undeveloped open space. Once considered a remote wasteland, it is now eyed hungrily by developers, housing commissioners, transportation officials and sanitation engineers, all with urgent (and mostly legitimate) needs for land, in this case because it is the only sizable vacant area left, land which must be reclaimed from the sea. And because it is all that is left, another bid is being made for the bay: conservationists and recreationists want its waters cleaned up, its spacious vistas left to nourish the eyes of city dwellers whose everyday vision is constricted into narrow street grid channels. If Jamaica Bay is saved — and the cost of saving it is admittedly expensive — it will be because enough people — politicians and citizens — want to preserve it as the twentieth century's legacy to the city's park system, realizing that time and land have run out, that Jamaica Bay represents the last chance for anything but relatively small accretions to that system.

There is, I think, in spite of the threat to Jamaica Bay and the continued pressure to encroach upon and diminish other municipal forests and wetlands, great hope for the continued presence of nature in the metropolis. Today, more and more, planning decisions are being made not only in City Hall but outside, in a kind of participatory planning process that is being conducted with growing expertise by community planning boards, citizens groups, block associations, civic organizations representing conservation and environmental interests, and motivated individuals championing pet projects, crusading for their vision of a greener and cleaner city. Already the preservation of certain park areas from encroachment or despoliation can be credited to the participatory citizen planners. Garbage trucks had begun to invade a section of the Pelham Bay salt marsh in 1967, when Bronx historian Theodore Kazimiroff hurriedly organized a citizens protest and conducted Parks Commissioner August Heckscher on a tour of the marsh. Converted to Kazimiroff's cause,

Heckscher agreed to rescind the agreement entered into by a previous administration which would have allowed the Department of Sanitation to take over the marsh.

Redesignation of the route planned for the Richmond Parkway on Staten Island — a route that would have shorn off hillcrests and filled in glacial ponds within the greenbelt — has occurred because a group of Staten Islanders organized themselves to do combat with federal and state highway officials. Fortunately they were able to enlist the sympathies of the Lindsay administration and to convince the mayor and his two successive park commissioners that the greenbelt should be not a highway but an urban trailway for hikers, horseback riders, cyclists and naturalists — again, a twentieth-century contribution to the parks legacy of New York City. Protracted studies and negotiations with transportation officials have resulted in the selection of a new and less ecologically damaging route for the highway.

Another hopeful sign is an as yet embryonic program being conducted by the Board of Education in cooperation with the city's natural science institutions. Under the auspices of the Environmental Resources Council it aims to provide a systematic approach to the teaching of ecology at all grade levels. Its focus is on teacher training, to educate teachers in methods of creating environmental awareness in the children, and to help them develop techniques for relating outdoor and museum field trip experiences to daily classroom activities and concerns. It will take a long time for this program to fully penetrate the vastly complicated New York City school system, but if successful it will create a future constituency for the city's forests and wetlands — a twenty-first-century constituency that will preserve the parks legacy and perhaps even add to it by restoring in places more fragments of the ecological heritage, that "green breast . . . that flowered once for Dutch sailors' eyes."

APPENDIX

DIRECTIONS TO THE PLACES DESCRIBED IN THIS BOOK

Courtesy of Parks, Recreation and Cultural Affairs Administration and
Transit Authority of New York City

INWOOD HILL PARK

LOCATION: 207th Street and Seaman Avenue, Manhattan.

PUBLIC TRANSPORTATION: IND subway "A" train to 207th Street station or IRT Broadway–7th Avenue subway to 168th Street and transfer to IND "A" train uptown to 207th Street.

BY CAR: Henry Hudson Parkway to Dyckman Street exit; follow Dyckman Street to Broadway; north on Broadway to 207th Street.

PELHAM BAY PARK

LOCATION: Adjacent to Long Island Sound, northeast Bronx.

PUBLIC TRANSPORTATION: IRT Lexington Avenue (Pelham Bay) line to Pelham Bay Park. Bus No. 12 from Fordham Road to Pelham Bay Park. Access to Hunter's Island from Orchard Beach parking lot; access to Goose Creek and Bartow Creek marsh areas from Split Rock Golf Course parking lot.

BY CAR: New England Thruway to Orchard Beach exit, then follow signs to Orchard Beach; or follow Pelham Bay Parkway to Shore Road north and the Split Rock Golf Course parking lot.

HIGH ROCK CONSERVATION CENTER

LOCATION: Rockland and Nevada avenues, Egbertville, Staten Island.

PUBLIC TRANSPORTATION: Staten Island Ferry to St. George Terminal; Bus R-111 to Rockland and Nevada avenues. Walk to park.

BY CAR: Verrazano-Narrows Bridge to Richmond Road–Clove Road exit. Turn left on Richmond Road to Rockland Avenue, watching for right angle in Richmond Road at Amboy Road; turn right on Rockland Avenue to Nevada Avenue; turn right on Nevada Avenue to park entrance.

BY CAR: Staten Island Ferry to St. George Terminal. Left on Bay Street to Vanderbilt Avenue; right on Vanderbilt Avenue; continue, after name changes to Richmond Road, to Rockland Avenue, watching for right angle in Richmond Road at Amboy Road; turn right on Rockland Avenue to Nevada Avenue, turn right on Nevada Avenue to park entrance. For information call (212) 987–6233.

149

WILLIAM T. DAVIS WILDLIFE REFUGE

LOCATION: Travis Avenue west of Richmond Avenue, New Springville, Staten Island.
PUBLIC TRANSPORTATION: Bus No. 114 travels along Richmond Avenue and can be reached at transfer points from Buses No. 102 and 107 leaving St. George Ferry Terminal.
BY CAR: From St. George Ferry Terminal turn right on Richmond Terrace to Morning-star Road (about five miles); turn left on Morningstar Road and follow to second traffic light; continue after name changes to Richmond Avenue, to Travis Avenue; turn right and continue for one block to refuge.
BY CAR: Verrazano-Narrows Bridge to Richmond Avenue exit; turn right on Richmond Avenue to Travis Avenue; turn right and continue for one block to refuge.

Appointments are necessary for groups of more than six people; guides and field trips can be arranged through Staten Island Museum, 75 Stuyvesant Place, St. George, Staten Island, New York 10301. Telephone: (212) 727-1135.

JAMAICA BAY WILDLIFE REFUGE

LOCATION: Cross Bay Boulevard between Howard Beach and Broad Channel, Queens.
PUBLIC TRANSPORTATION: IND Subway, Rockaway division, to Broad Channel Boulevard; or Green Line Bus to Cross Bay Boulevard.
BY CAR: Shore Parkway, Southern Parkway or Woodhaven Boulevard to Cross Bay Boulevard; south on Cross Bay Boulevard for approximately a mile and one half past North Channel Bridge to refuge parking lot.

Visitors must obtain a permit by writing to: Director, Maintenance and Operations, Parks Recreation and Cultural Affairs Administration, The Arsenal, 830 Fifth Avenue, New York, New York 10021.

WELFARE ISLAND

LOCATION: Middle of the East River opposite area between Forty-eighth and Eighty-sixth streets, Manhattan.
PUBLIC TRANSPORTATION: IRT to Queensboro Plaza or IND to Queens Plaza; then Bus No. 102 on the north side of street (Bridge Plaza North) to Welfare Island.
BY CAR: From Manhattan take upper level of the Queensboro Bridge; turn right at Welfare Island sign; turn right again on Twenty-first Street; drive north to second traffic light; and turn left for Welfare Island Bridge.

BIBLIOGRAPHY

GENERAL

Arbib, Robert S., Jr., Olin Sewall Pettingill, Jr., and Sally Hoyt Spofford for the Laboratory of Ornithology, Cornell University. *Enjoying Birds Around New York City*. Boston, 1966. An ornithological guide containing a useful set of park maps.

Board of Education of the City of New York, Bureau of Curriculum Development. *Operation New York: Using the Natural Environment of the City as a Curriculum Resource*. New York, 1960. A helpful manual for teachers, and parents too, who wish to show children how the processes of nature are continually at work even on a city sidewalk or in a schoolyard. Available from the Publication Sales Office of the Board of Education, 110 Livingston Street, Brooklyn, N.Y., 11201.

CHAPTER I

Danckaerts, Jasper. *Journal of Jasper Danckaerts 1679–1680*, edited by Bartlett Burleigh James and J. Franklin Jameson. New York, 1913.

Denton, Daniel. *A Brief Description of New York, With the Places Thereunto Adjoyning, Called The New Netherlands*. Reprinted from original edition of 1670. Cleveland, 1902.

DeVries, David Piertsz. "Voyage from Holland to America, A.D. 1632 to 1644," in *New York Historical Soc. Coll.*, 2d ser. Vol. III, Part I, New York, 1857.

Dickens, Charles. *American Notes*. New York, 1842.

Hill, George Everitt, and George E. Waring, Jr. "Old Wells and Water-Courses on the Island of Manhattan," Parts I and II of *Half Moon Series Papers on Historic New York*. New York, 1897. An informative description of the city's buried topography.

Juet, Robert. The Discovery of the Hudson River from "The Third Voyage of Master Henry Hudson Toward Nova Zemble . . ." Boston, 1898.

Kieran, John. *A Natural History of New York City*. Boston, 1959. That rare item, a reference book that is at once hugely informative and entertaining. It conveys on every page the author's delighted discovery of a wealth of wildlife within the chinks in the urban armor.

Matthiessen, Peter. *Wildlife in America*. New York, 1959. Chapter three portrays the incredible wealth of animal life inhabiting pre-urban eastern America.

Smith, James Reuel. *Springs and Wells of Manhattan and the Bronx, New York City, at the End of the Nineteenth Century*. New York, 1938.

Valentine, D. *Manual of the Corporation of the City of New York*. New York, 1842–1870. The various annual editions have good information about New York's pre-urban history.

Van der Donck, Adrian, in "Description of New-Netherlands," *Collections of the New York Historical Society*, 2d ser. Vol. I. New York, 1841. This volume also contains "Extracts from the Voyage of De Vries" and "Extracts from DeLaet's New-

World" as well as "Verrazano's voyage, A.D. 1524" and "Juet's Journal of Hudson's Voyage."

Wolley, Charles, A.M. *A Two Year's Journal in New York*. Reprinted from the original edition of 1701. Cleveland, 1902.

CHAPTER 2

Schuberth, Christopher J. *The Geology of New York City and Environs*. Garden City, New York, 1968. An excellent, up-to-date explanation of regional rock formation by a staff member of the American Museum of Natural History. A condensed version of the part of Dr. Schuberth's treatise relating to New York City is found in *Natural History* magazine, Vol. LXXVIII, No. 4, April 1969.

CHAPTER 3

Neiring, William A. *The Life of the Marsh*. New York, 1966. Part of "Our Living World of Nature" series, containing much useful information about the ecology of marshes.

Peters, George H. *The Trees of Long Island*. Publication No. 1 of the Long Island Historical Society, Summer, 1952. Has an informative description of the postglacial botanical formation of the area as well as a discussion of its arboreal showpieces.

Sirkin, Leslie A. "Late Pleistocene Pollen Stratigraphy of Western Long Island and Eastern Staten Island, New York," *Quaternary Paleoecology*, 1967. A technical paper describing an experiment in bog sediment analysis which throws considerable light on postglacial plant succession in New York City.

Teal, John and Mildred. *Life and Death of the Salt Marsh*. Boston, 1969. Traces the green ribbon of Atlantic coastal marshes from their beginnings to the present, focusing on their now rapidly accelerated destruction.

CHAPTER 4

Bolton, Reginald Pelham. *Washington Heights, Manhattan: Its Eventful Past*. New York, 1924. The definitive, if somewhat dryly written, source on the history of Inwood Park and its environs. Much of the material contained in it is found in two earlier accounts by Bolton: *The Indians of Washington Heights*, New York, 1909, and *Military Camp Life on Upper Manhattan Island and Adjacent Mainland During the American Revolution*, Albany, 1915. See also his *Inwood Hill Park on the Island of Manhattan*, New York, n.d.

DeVries's journal, "Voyage from Holland to America, A.D. 1632 to 1644," referred to above is a fascinating, often moving, first-hand account of the misguided policies of Director Kieft in relation to the Indians.

Von Krafft, John Charles Philip. "Journal of Lt. John Charles Philip Von Krafft, 1776–1784," in the *Collections of the New York Historical Society*, Vol. 15. New York, 1882. Offers a fascinating glimpse of the irony of eighteenth-century mercenary life with its pomp, prestige, social distinction, adventure, and money offered as inducements for career officers (the military being one of the few acceptable careers open to young European noblemen) and the harsh reality of the brutal, monotonous, bare-subsistence conditions in the field.

CHAPTER 5

Barr, Lockwood Anderson. *A Brief, But Most Complete and True Account of the Settlement of the Ancient Town of Pelham*. Richmond, 1947. A useful history of the Pell and Hunter families.

Bolton, Reginald Pelham. "The Home of Mistress Anne Hutchinson at Pelham, 1642–43," *New York Historical Society Quarterly*, Vol. 6, No. 2, July 1922.

Mullaly, John. *The New Parks Beyond the Harlem*. New York, 1887. A brief enumerating the advantages of acquisition of lands then outside of the city limits as city parks. See also: New York (State) Commission to Select and Locate Lands in the 23rd and 24th Wards of New York City. *Report to the New York Legislature of the Commission to Select and Locate Lands for Public Parks in the Twenty-third and Twenty-fourth Wards of the City of New York, and in the Vicinity Thereof*. New York, 1884.

CHAPTER 6

Abbot, Mabel. *The Life of William T. Davis*. Ithaca, New York, 1949. A readable biography of a passionate naturalist and leading authority on the cicada. Portions of Davis's journal are quoted throughout.

Davis, William T. *Days Afield on Staten Island*. New York, 1892. This little book of fresh impressionistic responses to nature on Staten Island makes one wish that Davis had spent more time writing in this vein.

Davis, William T., and Charles Leng. *Staten Island and Its People*. New York, 1930–33. The first two volumes contain much valuable information; the last three are "vanity biographies" of prominent local residents.

Early impressions of the island's scenery are contained in the following four accounts:

Kalm, Peter. *Travels in North America*. New York, 1966.

Olmsted, Frederick Law, Jr., and Theodora Kimball, eds. *Frederick Law Olmsted, Landscape Architect 1822–1903*. Vol. I. New York, 1922.

Fein, Albert, ed. *Landscape into Cityscape: Frederick Law Olmsted's Plans for a Greater New York City*. Ithaca, New York, 1967.

Thoreau, Henry David. *Correspondence*. Edited by Walter Harding and Carl Bode. New York, 1958.

CHAPTER 7

The works of Daniel Denton and Jasper Danckaerts cited above in the "General" section contain descriptions of Jamaica Bay. Later writings about the area are confined mostly to magazine articles and newspaper reports.

CHAPTER 8

The historian of Welfare Island also must rely heavily on journalistic accounts. Among the most interesting of these is a set of two articles by W. H. Davenport, "Blackwell's Island Lunatic Asylum," *Harper's Magazine*, No. CLXXXIX, Vol. XXXII, February 1866; and "The Work-House Blackwell's Island," *Harper's Magazine*, No. CXCVIII, Vol. XXXII, November 1866. See also Dickens, *American Notes*, referred to above. A concise account of the island's ownership from colonial times through successive generations of Blackwells up until the sale of the island to the city in 1823 is contained in "Blackwell's Island," *New York Historical Society Quarterly*, Vol. 5, No. 2, July 1921.

Plans for the island's future development are outlined in the following two reports:

Johnson, Philip, and Burgee, John. "The Island Nobody Knows," October 1969.

Welfare Island Planning and Development Committee, Benno Schmidt, Chairman. "Report of the Welfare Island Planning and Development Committee," February 1969.

INDEX

155

160

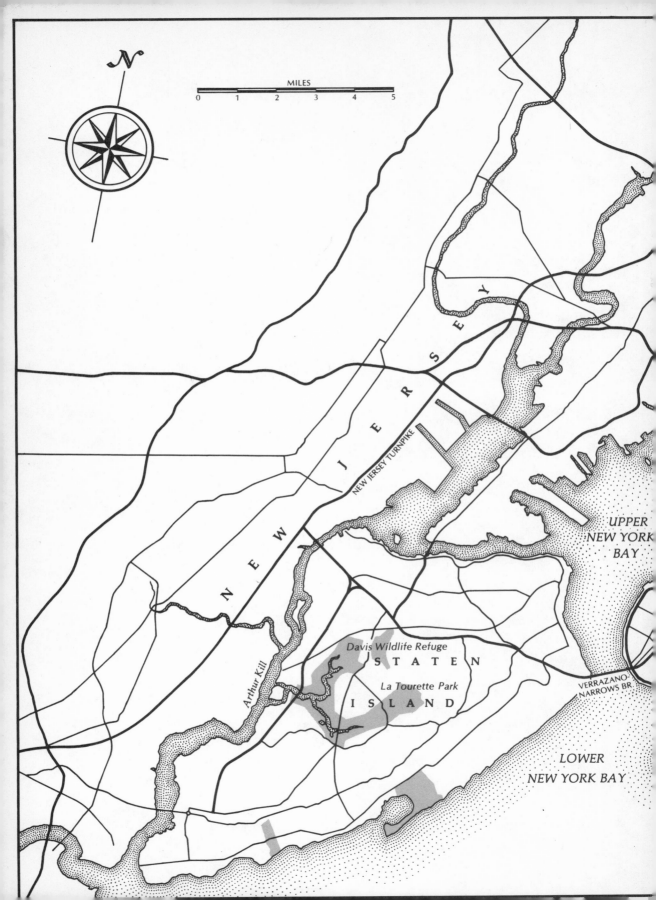

N

MILES

0 1 2 3 4 5

NEW JERSEY

NEW JERSEY TURNPIKE

Arthur Kill

Davis Wildlife Refuge

S T A T E N

La Tourette Park

I S L A N D

UPPER
NEW YORK
BAY

VERRAZANO-
NARROWS BR.

LOWER
NEW YORK BAY